BLUEPRINTS

Science Assessment Key Stage 2

Ron Adams

Stanley Thornes (Publishers) Ltd

Do you receive *BLUEPRINTS NEWS*?

Blueprints is an expanding series of practical teacher's ideas books and photocopiable resources for use in primary schools. Books are available for separate infant and junior age ranges for every core and foundation subject, as well as for an ever widening range of other primary teaching needs. These include **Blueprints Primary English** books and **Blueprints Resource Banks**. **Blueprints** are carefully structured around the demands of National Curriculum in England and Wales, but are used successfully by schools and teachers in Scotland, Northern Ireland and elsewhere.

Blueprints provide:
- *Total curriculum coverage*
- *Hundreds of practical ideas*
- *Books specifically for the age range you teach*
- *Flexible resources for the whole school or for individual teachers*
- *Excellent photocopiable sheets – ideal for assessment and children's work profiles*
- *Supreme value*

Books may be bought by credit card over the telephone and information obtained on **(01242) 577944**. Alternatively, photocopy and return this **FREEPOST** form to receive **Blueprints News**, our regular update on all new and existing titles. You may also like to add the name of a friend who would be interested in being on the mailing list.

Please add my name to the **BLUEPRINTS NEWS** mailing list.

Mr/Mrs/Miss/Ms _____

Home address _____

_____ Postcode _____

School address _____

_____ Postcode _____

Please also send **BLUEPRINTS NEWS** to:

Mr/Mrs/Miss/Ms _____

Address _____

_____ Postcode _____

To: Marketing Services Dept., Stanley Thornes Ltd, FREEPOST (GR 782), Cheltenham, GL50 1BR

Text © Ron Adams 1994

Original line illustrations © ST(P) Ltd 1994

The right of Ron Adams to be identified as author of this work has been asserted by him in accordance with the Copyright, Designs and Patents Act 1988.

Acknowledgements: The author wishes to thank Julia Hawkins, Science Co-ordinator at Walwayne Court School, Trowbridge, and Geoff Cresswell, Schools Science Inspector, for their help in the preparation of this book.

First published in 1994
First published in new binding in 1997 by
Stanley Thornes (Publishers) Ltd
Ellenborough House
Wellington Street
CHELTENHAM GL50 1YW

98 99 00 01 / 10 9 8 7 6 5 4 3 2

A catalogue record for this book is available from the British Library.

ISBN 0–7487–3447–3

Typeset by John Youé Books Design
Printed and bound in Great Britain by
Redwood Books, Trowbridge, Wiltshire

Contents

Introduction

An important part of a teacher's work is the constant assessment of children's learning. Only by assessing can we decide what children should do next and give them tasks that are appropriate. It is to support teachers in their assessment of children's work in science that this book has been written. The assessment tasks are intended to support teachers in forming their own assessments of what children know and can do. The exercises are not intended as rigorous in-depth 'tests'. Rather, they are indicators or clues to where the children have reached, and they are intended to have a predominantly formative purpose. The tasks employ a range of learning modes; many employ practical work and experimentation, others are more paper-based, but overall we have tried to provide opportunities for hands-on work either to introduce or to follow-up the task even where the assessment itself only uses information on the copymaster. All the activities have been tried and tested in schools to ensure that they work; many have been modified and adapted in the light of classroom testing.

USING BLUEPRINTS SCIENCE ASSESSMENT

Blueprints Science Assessment is a practical teacher's resource specifically tied in to the requirements of the National Curriculum for science in primary schools. It offers assessment tasks which teachers can use alongside those they devise themselves, or with more formal 'tests'. *Blueprints Science Assessment: Key Stage 1* provides tasks for children between 5 and 7 years old; *Blueprints Science Assessment: Key Stage 2* provides tasks for children between 7 and 11 years old. Teacher's notes and assessment copymasters are combined in one book for each Key Stage. The sequence the exercises follow matches that of the content of *Science in the National Curriculum (1995)*.

Blueprints Science Assessment: Key Stage 2 provides a set of assessment tasks through Key Stage 2. The assessment exercises are arranged in four sections, each related to the assessment of work expected of children through this Key Stage: Attainment Targets 1, 2, 3, and 4 at Levels 2–5. Although there are frequent opportunities to observe children's grasp of AT1 (Experimental and Investigative Science) whilst working on assessments for the other Attainment Targets, we have provided a bank of assessment purely focused on this AT and using contexts drawn from the other areas of science.

At the start of the teacher's notes about the assessment tasks relating to each Level of each Attainment Target there is an extract from the Statutory Orders, comprising the Attainment Target title, and the appropriate Level Description. For each assessment task there are two copymasters. The first of these is labelled 'A'. This is the key assessment sheet for that part of the curriculum. For all tasks there are also reassessment copymasters, labelled 'B'. Each of these appears immediately after each 'first try' copymaster, and closely follows the content of the A sheet with different examples. The reassessment sheets can be used in a number of different ways:

- for children to do as an addition to the first assessment task
- where children make mistakes on the first task, as a second try at a later date
- where a group of children are doing the task at the same time some can be given the A sheet and others the B sheet

The tasks call for varying amounts of preparation and resources but all provide opportunities to develop practical work if required and can be embedded into your ongoing science work as part of a lively and practical programme. The organization of the tasks is usually for each child to work individually, although some do require paired work to keep the resources required to a feasible level. You will find that each task has a key question which will enable you to focus on the core behaviour or skill which the child needs to demonstrate. The sheets usually involve direct pupil completion, but some, particularly at the lower levels, require teacher observation and written comment.

RECORD KEEPING

There are two summary record sheets at the back of the book. The first is a tick list to enable you to record which children in the class have done each task at a specific Level. The second is a tick list that can be kept for each child, showing those tasks the child has tried and which of them the child has completed successfully. Photocopy one Record Sheet 1 per class to maintain a tick list to show assessment tasks tried at a specific Level. Photocopy one Record Sheet 2 per child and tick the assessment tasks tried, those done successfully and reassessment attempts where appropriate. This record sheet can be added to school records.

How to use this book

This book has been tied to National Curriculum Attainment Targets so that the assessment tasks can be accessed easily. Within each of the sections – experimental and investigative science, life processes and living things, materials and their properties, and physical processes – the tasks have been arranged by Level, with Level 1 exercises first, and so on. Our intention has been to provide a bank of short assessment tasks covering all Attainment Targets. However, we hope that readers will, rather than taking the book wholesale, choose and use those tasks which they find most useful, to support their own assessment judgements.

The resources required for some of the tasks on the copymasters may be obtained from the usual suppliers of school equipment. Alternatively, library and museum services and the Museum Education Association may be able to provide appropriate materials and equipment or be able to provide information about suitable suppliers.

The copymasters (labelled 'A') are also marked to indicate to which AT and Level they refer. Reassessment copymasters are labelled 'B'. At the end of the book are two record sheets, enabling you to keep a class record and a record of the assessment tasks tried by each child.

AT1: Experimental and Investigative Science

Level Description

Pupils respond to suggestions of how to find things out and, with help, make their own suggestions. They use simple equipment provided and make observations related to their task. They compare objects, living things and events they observe. They describe their observations and record them using simple tables where it is appropriate to do so. They say whether what has happened was what they expected.

TASK 1 — RESPONDING AND PREDICTING A/B
C1-2

TASK 2 — DESCRIBE AND RECORD OBSERVATIONS A/B
C3-4

Resources
Copymaster C1, liquid water-colours (including yellow, red, and blue), teaspoons (5 ml) for measuring, palettes, brushes, pencils, clean water.

Organization
Each child works individually.

What you do
Discuss copymaster C1 and explain the task which is to predict and name the colours that will be produced in the investigation. Encourage the children to predict which colours will result when equal quantities of two colours are mixed – yellow and blue (green), yellow and red (orange), and blue and red (purple) – and to suggest how to test whether their predictions are correct. Use teaspoons to measure equal amounts of ready-mixed colours. Get the children to mix the colours and paint a swatch as part of their predictions. Ask them to write down the names of the colours.

What the child does
Each child predicts and then tests their predictions, using spoons to measure quantities, and investigating which colours result when mixed as above, and records their predictions and the results.

Key question
Can children respond to suggestions of how to find things out and make their own predictions?

Reassessment
Give the child copymaster C2, liquid water-colours (including red, purple, blue and green), spoons for measuring, palettes, brushes, pencils, clean water.

Resources
Copymaster C3, a collection of objects including a ping-pong ball, cork, stone, piece of wood, Plasticine ®, an orange, a Lego ® brick, small piece of card, a pencil and a nail.

Organization
Children may work individually or in pairs; you should monitor individual contributions.

What you do
Explain the tasks which are to predict which objects will sink or float by matching pictures to the correct bowl, test them and record the results, score how many correct predictions were made. Encourage the children to think about what kinds of material might float and why. Can some metal things float?

What the child does
Each child predicts which objects will float and which will sink, draws their prediction on the copymaster matching the pictures and carries out the test, makes a simple table of the results by drawing the things tested in the correct box, and records the success rate out of 10.

Key question
Can children make their own predictions, make observations and record the results of the test?

Reassessment
Use copymaster C4, a collection of objects including tennis ball, pill bottle with lid, a key, felt-tip pen, apple, screw, plastic animal, fir-cone, small metal car and a jam jar lid (upside down).

LEVEL
3

Level Description

Pupils respond to suggestions, put forward their own ideas and, where appropriate, make simple predictions. They make relevant observations and measure quantities, such as length or mass, using a range of simple equipment. With some help they carry out a fair test, recognising and explaining why it is fair. They record their observations in a variety of ways. They provide explanations for observations and, where they occur, for simple patterns in recorded measurements. They say what they have found out from their work.

TASK 3
C5-6

ANSWER QUESTIONS, MAKE PREDICTIONS A/B

Resources
Copymaster C5, jelly, cooker, chocolate, wax crayons, apples, uncooked pasta.

Organization
This is a teacher-led investigation (individual and class).

What you do
Explain the tasks which are to circle items on the copymaster that would melt in the fingers, predict what will happen if wax is gently heated on a cooker, whether jelly or wax will melt first when heated, to predict whether chocolate can become solid again once melted. Tell the children that you will demonstrate the activities which require the use of heat after they have completed the tasks.

What the child does
The children make simple predictions, complete the tasks on the copymaster and watch the teacher-led investigations into melting and solidifying.

Key question
Can the children suggest questions and ideas and make predictions based on everyday experience which can be tested? The predictions should contain the word 'because' in order to relate to everyday experiences.

Reassessment
Use copymaster C6, cooker, butter, biscuits, rice, carrots, jelly, chocolate, cheese and wax.

TASK 4
C7-8

FAIR TEST USING SIMPLE EQUIPMENT A/B

Resources
Copymaster C7, supply of small pots, bean seeds, water, soil, labels, rulers.

Organization
Each child works individually.

What you do
Explain the tasks which are to predict whether a bean

will germinate and grow better when given water, choose simple equipment that will be needed to fair test the predictions, describe with diagrams how the fair test will be undertaken, how growth of the plant will be measured, and record what happens to both beans after a period of three weeks. Encourage the children to observe and record the seedlings' growth and discuss what is happening.

What the child does
Each child carries out the investigation to see if seeds grow better in watered conditions. They measure and record the seedlings' growth with standard measuring tools (rulers) and complete the tasks on the copymaster.

Key question
Can the child make measurements with a standard measuring tool such as a ruler? Can they quantify a variable which changes over time, as well as making discontinuous measurements? Do they understand how a fair test could be carried out (under teacher direction – where should the ruler be placed and viewed from each time to make the investigation fairer)?

Reassessment
Use copymaster C8, bean seeds, rulers, flower pots, labels, soil, natural light, water. C8 is similar to C7 except children predict and investigate whether bean seeds will germinate and grow better when planted in soil.

TASK 5
C9-10

MEASURE, NOTICE PATTERNS, MAKE REPORT A/B

Resources
Copymaster C9, supply of small dishes, cress seeds, water, soil, labels, Sellotape ®, rulers, copymaster C9.

Organization
Each child works individually.

What you do
Get the children to germinate two sets of cress seeds under ideal conditions. Once they have sprouted, maintain the growing conditions for one set while halting the watering of the other set of cress sproutings but maintain all other conditions. Give out copymaster C9 and explain the tasks which are to investigate whether seedlings grow better with or without water, to make daily observations of the experiments for a week, and to record the results. Get the children to make observations of the height of

the seedlings. Encourage them to present their findings by drawing bar charts, to see if they notice any patterns of growth and appearance of plants, and to say what happens and why.

What the child does
The child carries out the investigation, draws diagrams of what the two sets of seedlings look like after a week, records results in tabular form, draws a bar chart, and reports findings.

Key question
Can children present data in various ways? At first through drawings, later by putting data in a table which has already been drafted for them, for example a simple two-column table. Are the children able to put data on a simple bar chart where axes and scale are already drawn for them and labelled? Are children able to interpret information from their investigation and distinguish between what they have observed and how and why things happened?

Reassessment
Use copymaster C10, supply of small dishes, cress seeds, water, soil, labels, Sellotape ®, rulers. The reassessment is similar to the work on copymaster C9 but when the cress seeds have sprouted, maintain the growing conditions for one set while placing the other set of cress seedlings in a light-tight box or cupboard. Keep all other conditions the same and investigate whether seedlings grow better with or without daylight.

Level Description

LEVEL 4

Pupils recognise the need for fair tests, describing, or showing in the way they perform their task, how to vary one factor whilst keeping others the same. Where appropriate, they make predictions. They select suitable equipment to use and make a series of observations and measurements that are adequate for the task. They present their observations and measurements clearly, using tables and bar charts. They begin to plot points to form simple graphs and use these graphs to point out and interpret patterns or trends in their data. They take account of these patterns when they draw conclusions, and begin to relate their conclusions to scientific knowledge and understanding.

TASK 6 C11 -12

FAIR TEST VARYING ONE FACTOR (1) A/B

Resources
Teeth, distilled water, three soft drinks which contain sugar such as branded colas and fizzy fruit-flavoured drinks, magnifying glass, measuring cylinders (same amount of liquid in each case), copymaster C11.

Organization
The children may work individually or in pairs; monitor individual input.

What you do
Contact a local dentist or dental hospital to get a supply of sterile teeth. Otherwise, use small pieces of chicken bone. Discuss the health of teeth, the bad effect sugar has upon them and which foods contain sugar. Give out the copymaster C11 and explain the task which is to make predictions about the effect of different branded drinks and pure water on teeth, theorise and test their theories, and record the results. Ask questions such as 'Do the drinks attack teeth? What will happen to the teeth? Why?'.

What the child does
The child makes predictions, ensures fair testing (with help), investigates whether drinks damage teeth by immersing teeth in the four drinks for a period of a week, tests theories, records results by making annotated drawings and explains the results orally.

Key question
Can children ask questions, suggest ideas and make predictions based on relevant knowledge and in a form that can be investigated? (Actual knowledge is needed to be able to say that the sugar in soft drinks damages teeth whilst water does not.)

Reassessment
Use copymaster C12, teeth, black coffee without sugar, black coffee with one sugar, black coffee with three sugars, black coffee with six sugars. The task on copymaster C12 is similar to that on copymaster C11.

TASK 7 C13 -14

FAIR TEST VARYING ONE FACTOR (2) A/B

Resources
Clear jars, iron nail, piece of plastic, pebble, piece of copper pipe, water, copymaster C13.

Organization
Each child works individually.

What you do
Give out copymaster C13 and explain the task which is to immerse each material in a jar of clean water for a period of a week, predict what will happen and record the results. Discuss how iron rusts. The task involves testing predictions. Encourage the children to suggest ideas for testing their predictions. For example, they may put all

the samples alongside each other in the same conditions of light and heat.

What the child does
The child makes predictions, ensures that the conditions are the same and that only one variable is changed, eg the sample material being tested, and completes the task on copymaster C13 and records the results of the investigation.

Key question
Can the child ask questions, suggest ideas and make predictions based on relevant knowledge and in a form that can be investigated?

Reassessment
Use copymaster C14.

TASK 8 GRAPHS, PATTERNS AND TRENDS A/B
C15 -16

Resources
Copymaster C15, measuring tape, pencils.

Organization
The children work as a class and in pairs.

What you do
Explain the task which is to see if there is any relation between foot size and hand span of pupils (explain what hand span is). Explain the investigation and the objectives that include a good experimental approach combined with presentation and interpretation of results. Children should measure foot size (length) and hand span in a sci-

entific way, eg agree to round up all fractions of a millimetre and to stand so that eyes line up with the edges of each child's hand or foot when measuring, to avoid problems of incorrect readings caused by parallax. Give out copies of the copymaster C15. All the results can be put on a class chart which can be used for the construction of tables by the children who then plot graphs on the copymaster. Demonstrate how each pupil's foot size and hand span can be shown as a simple small cross placed where the two factors intersect on the graph.

What the child does
The children carry out the investigation into the size of feet and hand spans of class members (working in pairs and double checking results – are finger and thumb fully stretched apart?), make their own records in their own constructed tables on separate pieces of paper, plots information about all pupils' feet sizes and hand spans on the graph on the copymaster (unaided), and notice patterns in results and draw conclusions.

Key question
Can children construct and label their own tables and enter data correctly? Are children able to plot information on the graph which is given on the copymaster (with no assistance), using data involving whole numbers? Can children notice patterns and record results ? Are they able to draw conclusions which link patterns and observations or results to the original question in the investigation (prediction or idea), eg do children with big feet have larger hand spans?

Reassessment
Use copymaster C16. The reassessment is similar to the task on copymaster C15 except that children investigate whether there is a link between hair colour and eye colour. Do not do comparative work on height and weight as these are very emotive areas.

Level Description

Pupils identify the key factors they need to consider in contexts that involve only a few factors. Where appropriate, they make predictions based on their scientific knowledge and understanding. They select apparatus for a range of tasks and use it with care. They make a series of observations or measurements with precision appropriate to the task. They begin to repeat observations and measurements and to offer simple explanations for any differences they encounter. They record observations and measurements systematically and present data as line graphs. They draw conclusions that are consistent with the evidence and begin to relate these to scientific knowledge and understanding.

TASK 9 USE KNOWLEDGE, MAKE PREDICTIONS A/B
C17 -18

Resources
Butter, stove, pan, stop clock, weighing scales, copymaster C17.

Organization
The children work in groups or as a class.

What you do
This requires close supervision. Give out copymaster C17 and explain the tasks which are to measure out the 20 g samples of butter, and predict what will happen when 20 g of butter are heated over varying degrees of heat. Undertake five investigations but vary the temperature. Link the children's prediction to the relationships between variables. For example, the higher the temperature, the more quickly the butter will melt because it will quickly change from a solid to liquid as the molecules heat up and move apart.

What the child does

The children consider the factors which affects the speed at which butter melts – such as the original temperature of the butter, the heat applied and the quantity of the butter used – and measure out carefully the butter into 20 g pieces, make predictions and test them, and record the results on a bar chart and draw conclusions.

Key question

Can children base hypotheses on scientific knowledge, understanding or a theory? Can children include the cause in a hypothesis, for example 'the higher the temperature the quicker it will melt', and the effect, such as 'because the higher temperature will quickly turn the butter from solid to liquid as the molecules heat up and move apart'?

Reassessment

Use copymaster C18, butter, stove, pan, stop clock, weighing scales. The tasks on copymaster C18 are similar to those on C17 except that children investigate what happens when 20 g of butter are heated with varying degrees of heat with or without stirring. This experiment requires close supervision for safety reasons.

TASK 10 — IDENTIFY KEY FACTORS A/B
C19-20

Resources

Copymaster C19.

Organization

Each child works individually.

What you do

Give out copymaster C19 and explain the task which is to identify and circle the key factors on the copymaster. Take time to discuss and explore the reasons for the choices made by the children after the copymaster tasks have been completed.

What the child does

Each child identifies the key factors for each event from those written on the copymaster, circles them, and discusses the reasons for the choices made.

Key question

Can children identify key factors that they need to consider in contexts that involve only a few factors?

Reassessment

Use copymaster C20.

TASK 11 — REPEATED OBSERVATIONS, LINE GRAPHS A/B
C21-22

Resources

Ping-pong balls, chalk, rulers, tapes or an accurate scale fixed to the wall, copymaster C21.

Organization

The children work in pairs; monitor individual input.

What you do

Give out copymaster C21 and explain the tasks which are to explain what happens in the diagram of the copymaster, to measure accurately what happens in section two of the copymaster and repeat the experiment three times, to review these three experiments and see if the results are the same and to explain any differences. You should explain that it will be easier to measure the first, second and third bounces individually rather than all in one go. Ask before the investigation what the children think will happen and why? Do they think that the result from one test will be reliable? Why should the test be repeated? Get pupils to identify the dependent variables they are to measure such as the height of each bounce They have to control variables so as to ensure a fair test, for example by ensuring that the same ball is dropped from the correct height each time.

What the child does

The children complete the tasks on the copymaster.

Key question

Can children set up reliable repeatable tests, record results and explain any differences between the results.

Reassessment

Use copymaster C22, tennis balls, chalk, rulers, tapes or an accurate scale fixed to a wall, different floor surfaces eg concrete, wood, grass (near a wall for measuring bounce heights).

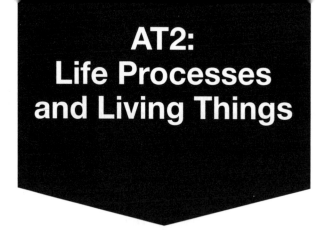

AT2: Life Processes and Living Things

LEVEL 2

Level Description

Pupils use their knowledge about living things to describe basic conditions, such as a supply of food, water, air or light, that animals and plants need in order to survive. They recognise that living things grow and reproduce. They sort living things into groups, using simple features. They describe the basis for their groupings in terms such as number of legs or shape of leaf. They recognise that different living things are found in different places, such as ponds or woods.

TASK 1
C23 -24

CONDITIONS FOR PLANT GROWTH A/B

Resources
Three bean plants per group/class, water, jugs, light-tight box, box with one side removed, window sill and copymaster C23.

Organization
The children work in groups or as a class.

What you do
Give the children copymaster C23 and explain the task which is to identify light as one of the basic conditions that plants need to grow healthily. Ask children to predict what they think will happen over a period of time, when all plants receive the same amount of water and are kept reasonably warm, whilst one plant is kept in the dark (in a light-tight box), one is in broad daylight on a window sill and the other is in a closed box with one window cut in an end. Ask children questions such as 'Which bean plant will grow the best? How shall we measure how much the plants grow?'. Help children to draw conclusions.

What the child does
The child predicts what will happen to the three plants, sets up the experiment, observes over a period of time, and records the results and draws conclusions.

Key question
Do children understand that most plants need light to survive and remain healthy? Do they know the basic conditions that plants need in order to survive?

Reassessment
Use copymaster C24, three bean plants per group/class, water, jugs. The task on copymaster C24 is similar to that on C25 except that children experiment to identify that

the right amount of water is one of the basic conditions that plants need to grow healthily.

TASK 2
C25 -26

ANIMAL LIFE PROCESSES A/B

Resources
Copymaster C25.

Organization
Each child works individually.

What you do
Give out copymaster C25 and explain the task which is to identify which things all animals need in order to stay alive.

What the child does
Each child completes copymaster C25.

Key question
Do children know that animals need food, water, air, warmth and shelter in order to survive?

Reassessment
Use copymaster C26.

TASK 3
C27 -28

LIVING THINGS AND THEIR HOMES A/B

Resources
Copymaster C27.

Organization
Each child works individually.

What you do
Give out copymaster C27 and explain the task which is to match each plant to its home on the copymaster, to explain their choices, and to suggest and draw two more plants and their homes.

What the child does
Each child completes the tasks.

Key question
Do children recognize that different plants are found in different places?

Reassessment
Use copymaster C28 for animals and their homes.

TASK 4 — ANIMAL AND PLANT GROUPS A/B
C29 -30

Resources
Copymaster C29, reference books.

Organization
Each child works individually.

What you do
Give out copymaster C29 and explain the tasks which are to use books to research birds and mammals, to group the animals in the pictures as either birds or mammals and join the labels to the correct picture, to name two more mammals and two more birds, and write down in which way birds and mammals are different.

What the child does
Completes the tasks in the copymaster.

Key question
Do children recognize that animals can be sorted using simple features?

Reassessment
Use copymaster C30. The tasks on copymaster C30 are similar to those on C29 except that it deals with plants instead of animals.

TASK 5 — REPRODUCTION A/B
C31 -32

Resources
Copymaster C31.

Organization
Each child works individually.

What you do
Give out copymaster C31 and explain the task which is to use reference books to find the appropriate mothers of the animals, cut out the illustrations and stick mother and young together on a separate piece of paper or card.

What the child does
The child completes the task in the copymaster.

Key question
Do children recognize that living things grow and reproduce?

Reassessment
Use copymaster C32. Children find the pictures of the correct mothers, draw and name them. Resources: reference books, pencils.

LEVEL 3 — Level Description

Pupils use their knowledge of basic life processes, such as growth or reproduction, when they describe differences between living and non-living things. They provide simple explanations for changes in living things, such as diet affecting the health of humans or other animals, or lack of light or water altering plant growth. They identify ways in which an animal is suited to its environment, such as a fish having fins to help it swim.

TASK 6 — LIVING AND NON-LIVING THINGS A/B
C33 -34

Resources
Copymaster C33.

Organization
The children work individually or in groups.

What you do
Provide newspaper front pages for analysis into living and non-living categories. Give out copies of copymaster C33 and explain the tasks which are to analyse a newspaper front page listing all living and non-living things mentioned, to form two galleries, living and non-living, and identify what all living things have in common by colouring the appropriate petals. Discuss the reasons for the children's choices.

What the child does
The child completes the tasks.

Key question
Do children know the basic life processes common to all living things?

Reassessment

Use copymaster C34. The tasks on copymaster C34 are similar to those on C33. Using the copymaster children circle the things that humans need to grow, they identify ways in which living and non-living things are different, and name and draw two non-living things.

TASK 7 — SUITABLE ANIMAL HOMES A/B
C35-36

Resources
Copymaster C35.

Organization
Each child works individually.

What you do
Give out copies of copymaster C35 and explain the task which is to say why various animals are suited to the environments in which they live.

What the child does
The child gives reasons of how and why animals in the picture are suited to the environment in which they live; for example fish have fins to swim with.

Key question
Can children identify ways in which animals have adapted to their environment?

Reassessment
Use copymaster C36.

LEVEL 4

Level Description

Pupils demonstrate knowledge and understanding of aspects of life processes and living things drawn from the Key Stage 2 or Key Stage 3 programme of study. They use scientific names for some major organs of body systems, such as the circulatory system, and identify the position of these organs in the human body. They identify organs, such as petal, stamen or stigma, of different plants they observe. They use keys based on observable external features to help them to identify and group living things systematically. They recognise that feeding relationships exist between plants and animals in a habitat, and describe these relationships, using food chains and terms such as predator and prey.

TASK 8 — NAME AND POSITION HUMAN ORGANS A/B
C37-38

Resources
Large pieces of paper for children to lie on, chalks, pencils, copymaster C37, reference books.

Organization
In pairs, children draw round each other and then complete the task individually.

What you do
Explain the tasks which are to draw round their partners bodies and to mark and label the main organs (using reference books), and to use this information and complete copymaster C37.

What the child does
The child draws round the outline of their partner to give a body shape, draws in the position and approximate size and shape of the heart, lungs, stomach, kidneys and liver, and labels the organs, then completes copymaster C37.

Key question
Can children correctly identify and locate their heart, lungs, stomach, kidneys and liver?

Reassessment
Use copymaster C38, coloured pencils, reference books, glue. The tasks on C38 are similar to those on C37 except that the children colour, cut out and assemble the different body parts and make a model of the human respiratory system with labelled parts. The labels should be: 1 breastbone, 2 collar bone, 3 front ribs, 4 lungs, 5 heart, 6 windpipe, 7 backbone, 8 back ribs, 9 shoulder blades. As a further practical assessment activity, ask the children to make a body box using a cereal box as a torso and make relative-sized organs to go inside. These can be made from papier maché or clay.

TASK 9 — IDENTIFY ORGANS OF PLANTS A/B
C39-40

Resources
Flowers from the school grounds, magnifying glasses, reference books, copymaster C39.

Organization
Each child works individually.

What you do
Allow children time to study flowers from the school grounds before they start the task; discuss the organs of plants with them. Give out copies of copymaster C39 and

explain the task which is to draw in and label flower parts in the flower picture frame.

What the child does
Uses magnifying glasses to study flowers from the school grounds and name their parts (stigma, style, ovary, stamen, stem and petal), draws (using colour) and labels the flower and its parts on copymaster C39.

Key question
Can children locate and name major parts of flowering plants?

Reassessment
Use copymaster C40, reference books. As a further practical assessment children can build a model flower with its major organs.

TASK 10 — USE KEYS TO GROUP LIVING THINGS A/B
C41 -42

Resources
Rose, daffodil, bean, carrot, copymaster C41.

Organization
Each child works individually.

What you do
Give out copies of the copymaster and revise how to use a key. Explain the task which is to identify, using the key, which plant should go in the correct place.

What the child does
The child uses the copymaster and completes the task.

Key question
Can the child use keys effectively?

Reassessment
Use copymaster C42, six minibeasts from school grounds (ensure that they are well cared for), magnifying glasses, reference books. The task on copymaster C42 is similar to that on C41 except using minibeasts instead of plants – the key should be constructed on a separate piece of paper.

TASK 11 — FOOD CHAINS A/B
C43 -44

Resources
Copymaster C43.

Organization
Each child works individually.

What you do
Give out copymaster C43 and explain the tasks which are to use arrows to show the food chains in each of the four drawings, write the words 'predator' and 'prey' by the appropriate living things, and make up and illustrate their own food chains.

What the child does
The child completes the tasks on copymaster C43.

Key questions
Can the child explain relationships in a food chain? Can they identify predators and preys?

Reassessment
Use copymaster C44, glue, scissors, coloured pencils, paper or thin card.

LEVEL 5

Level Description
Pupils demonstrate an increasing knowledge and understanding of aspects of life processes and living things drawn from the Key Stage 2 or Key Stage 3 programme of study. They describe the main functions of some organs of the human body, such as the heart, and of the flowering plant, such as the petal, stamen or stigma. They explain how these functions are essential to the organism. They describe the main stages of the life cycles of humans and flowering plants and point out similarities. They recognise that there is great variety of living things and understand the importance of classification. They explain that different organisms are found in different habitats because of differences in environmental factors, such as the availability of light or water.

TASK 12 — CHANGES IN LIVING THINGS – DIET A/B
C45 -46

Resources
Diet and health information from a local doctor, reference books, information about malnutrition from charitable organizations (Oxfam), copymaster C45.

Organization
Each child works individually.

What you do
Give copymaster C45 to the children and explain the tasks which are to record their daily menu and use reference books to categorize the meals containing protein, carbohydrates, fats and vitamins and minerals, and to give a simple explanation of why a balanced diet is needed. Remind

children of the four main food groups and what to include in their daily intake. Discuss the need to avoid too much sugar, fats and additives. Discuss the effect of malnutrition on our health and what a balanced diet is.

What the child does
The child completes the tasks in the copymaster.

Key question
Can the child explain that the body keeps healthy by eating the right kind and amount of food in a balanced diet? Can the child understand the changes that food (or lack of it) can bring about in their bodies and health, the way they look, feel and function?

Reassessment
Use copymaster C46, diet and health information, information about athletes and how they train, information about the importance of particular foods for athletes.

TASK 13 FUNCTIONS OF HUMAN ORGANS A/B
C47 -48

Resources
Copymaster C47.

Organization
Each child works individually.

What you do
Give children copymaster C47 and explain the tasks which are to explain the function of human organs using diagrams if necessary and to explain what happens if the human organs malfunction.

What the child does
The child explains how the different human organs function in as much detail as possible, and what happens if the human organs do not function properly.

Key question
Can the child describe the main functions of the human organs? Does the child know what happens when the organs do not function properly?

Reassessment
Use copymaster C48. As an additional assessment activity get the children to draw a body outline and then draw and label where the organs are positioned in the body.

TASK 14 FUNCTIONS OF FLOWERING PLANT ORGANS A/B
C49 -50

Resources
Flowers form the school grounds, scalpel or sharp craft knife for adult use, reference books, magnifying glasses, coloured pencils, copymaster C49.

Organization
Each child works individually.

What you do
Give out copies of copymaster C49 and explain the tasks which are to collect examples of flowers that are suitable for pollination by insects, to examine closely the flowers (cross-sectioned by an adult using a knife) so that the internal organs can be examined using a magnifying glass, to draw and label the cross-section of the flower identifying main organs used in insect pollination, and to describe the main function of each of the labelled organs. Help the children to gather flowers. Children must not be allowed near sharp knives or scalpels.

What the child does
The child collects flowers from school grounds that are suitable for pollination by insects, examines the flowers, in cross-section, the internal organs using magnifying glass, and draws and labels the cross-section, identifying main organs used in insect pollination, then writes down the main functions of each of the labelled organs.

Key question
Can the child explain correctly how the flowers function in insect pollination? Can the child identify flowering plant organs? Can they explain how the functions of the organs are essential to the organism?

Reassessment
Use copymaster C50.

TASK 15 HUMAN LIFE CYCLE A/B
C51 -52

Resources
Copymaster C51.

Organization
The children may work individually or in pairs, but monitor individual input.

What you do
Give the children copymaster C51 and explain the tasks which are to name the stages in the female human life cycle using arrows to produce the correct time-line sequence, and to describe the different stages of female human life and explain how the life of a female human is similar to that of a flowering plant.

What the child does
The child completes tasks on copymaster C51.

Key question
Can the children describe the main stages of the human life cycle? Can children point out similarities between the life cycles of humans and flowering plants?

Reassessment
Use copymaster C52.

TASK 16 — LIFE CYCLES OF PLANTS A/B
C53-54

Resources
Copymaster C53, reference books.

Organization
Each child works individually.

What you do
Discuss similarities and differences between the seeds of a variety of plants. Give out copies of copymaster C53 and explain the tasks which are to describe the method of dispersal of seeds and how the seeds are pollinated to produce more plants. Show children a variety of flowers and their seeds, for example sycamore, sweet pea, beans and poppy. It is important to use reference books for this activity.

What the child does
The child observes similarities and differences between seeds, uses the copymaster, identifies the seeds and describes how they are dispersed and germinate.

Key question
Can the child describe the main stages of the life cycle of plants, including pollination, seed production, seed dispersal and germination?

Reassessment
Use copymaster C54, reference books.

TASK 17 — PREFERRED HABITATS A/B
C55-56

Resources
Woodlice, boxes to provide varied conditions such as dark/light conditions and dry/wet conditions, stop clocks, copymaster C55, magnifying glasses.

Organization
The children work in pairs (you need to monitor each child's input).

What you do
Give out copymaster C55 and explain the tasks which are to collect woodlice and draw one, to devise a test to find out whether woodlice prefer damp, dry, light, or dark conditions, to conduct the test and time how long the woodlice stay in the damp or dry environment, and to record the results making a table of bar charts for the different environments. Encourage the children to predict outcomes and give reasons for their choices. Ask questions such as 'How will you make your test a fair one? How will you record the results?'. (eg the amount of time spent in each area or moving to another area).

What the child does
The child collects woodlice from school grounds, makes

a detailed drawing of one, predicts what conditions they prefer, designs a series of fair tests to find out if the woodlice prefer damp or dry conditions and light or dark conditions, and times how long the woodlice spend in each area or moving between each area, and records the results and draws conclusions.

Key question
Can the children identify the conditions in which woodlice prefer to live?

Reassessment
Use copymaster C56, the school grounds, magnifying glasses, tally charts. The tasks on copymaster C56 are similar to those on C55 except that the children choose two habitats in the school grounds (eg pond, under logs or bark chips) to predict and investigate the kinds of creatures that live there.

TASK 18 — CLASSIFICATION OF LIVING THINGS A/B
C57-58

Resources
Copymaster C57, reference books.

Organization
Each child works individually.

What you do
Give out copymaster C57 and explain the task which is to classify all of the animals illustrated on the copymaster according to the classifications listed there.

What the child does
The child completes the classification tasks in the copymaster by cutting out the labels and the creatures, arranging them and sticking them on to a separate piece of paper.

Key question
Does the child recognize that there is a great variety of living things and do they understand the importance of classification?

Reassessment
Use copymaster C58, reference books. The task on copymaster C58 is similar to that on C57 except that the children classify living things into animals or plants.

AT3: Materials and their Properties

TASK 1 — IDENTIFYING COMMON MATERIALS A/B
C59 -60

Resources
Copymaster C59, balsa, tissue-paper, rubber bands, copper tubing, clear glass, clay, concrete and a plastic ruler.

Organization
Each child works individually.

What you do
Explain any unfamiliar terms and relate them to ones they know such as hard, flexible and rigid. Give out copies of copymaster C59 and explain the tasks which are to identify common materials by matching pictures to words, to predict which materials match the descriptive words 'rigid' and 'flexible' and arrange accordingly the materials into two groups. Show the children a wide range of materials.

What the child does
The child identifies the common materials and writes down which properties apply to each of them, and arranges the materials into two groups based on their properties (eg rigid or flexible).

Key question
Can the child identify common materials? Does the child know the properties of common materials?

Reassessment
Use copymaster C60, sheet metal, a magnifying glass, a window, a brick, sunglasses, a leaf, wood, a coloured bottle, tracing-paper, curtains, a glass of clean water, and a torch to provide a strong beam of light.

TASK 2 — MATERIAL PROPERTIES A/B
C61 -62

Resources
Copymaster C61, kitchen utensils including a selection of metal, wooden and plastic ones as shown on the copymaster.

Organization
Each child works individually.

What you do
Show the child a variety of kitchen utensils and discuss what they are made from (get them to predict what materials have been used) and why they are suitable for their purposes. Give out a copy of the copymaster and explain the tasks which are to identify the materials that the kitchen utensils are made from, to say why the materials are suitable for their uses, and to sort the utensils into sets, depending on what they are made from, using Venn diagrams.

What the child does
The child writes down what different kitchen utensils are made from, explains why the materials are suitable for the different uses, sorts utensils into groups according to which materials they are made from and sorts them using the Venn diagram on the copymaster, writing the appropriate letter in place (A, B, C, D, and E).

Key question
Can the child sort materials according to their properties?

Reassessment
Use copymaster C62 and as many of the following as possible (labelled): woollen jumper, cotton dress, silk scarf, linen pillow covers, nylon shirt, polyester dress or trousers, plastic place mats, two laundry baskets (or cardboard boxes) labelled made fabrics/natural fabrics.

Level Description

Pupils use their knowledge and understanding of materials when they describe a variety of ways of sorting them into groups according to their properties. They explain why some materials are particularly suitable for specific purposes, such as metal for making electrical cables. They recognise that some changes, such as the freezing of water, can be reversed and some, such as the baking of clay, cannot, and they classify changes in this way.

TASK
3
C63
-64

USE OF MATERIALS A/B

Resources
Copymaster C63, a selection of materials including wood, glass, steel, cotton and rubber, and reference books.

Organization
Each child works individually.

What you do
Give out copies of copymaster C63 and explain the task which is to provide two suggestions for the use of the materials listed and illustrated on the copymaster. Encourage the children to examine the collection of labelled raw materials before undertaking the task and to use reference books.

What the child does
The child writes down two suggestions for the use of the illustrated materials.

Key question
Can the child provide correct uses for a selection of given materials?

Reassessment
Use copymaster C64, a selection of materials including wood, clay, iron ore, wool and rubber sheeting.

TASK
4
C65
-66

REVERSIBLE/ IRREVERSIBLE CHANGES A/B

Resources
Copymaster C65, fridge, ice-cubes, saucers, stopwatch.

Organization
The children work in small groups.

What you do
Discuss how long it takes for an ice-cube to melt and ask questions such as 'Can you make an ice-cube melt quickly? Can you stop it melting?'. Encourage the children to make and record predictions, and encourage fair testing. Give out copies of copymaster C65 and explain the tasks which are to record how long it takes for six ice-cubes to melt in six different locations as on the copymaster, to suggest ways of stopping an ice-cube from melting, and to suggest how to remake an ice-cube from the one that has melted. When the tasks are completed, discuss the results.

What the child does
The children complete the tasks on the copymaster.

Key questions
Do the children know that the freezing of water can be reversed?

Reassessment
Use copymaster C66, 120 g flour, 60 g salt, warm water, two bowls. First the raw materials have to be described by the children, then they are mixed and baked and the rest of the task completed.

LEVEL 4

Level Description

Pupils demonstrate knowledge and understanding of aspects of materials and their properties drawn from Key Stage 2 or Key Stage 3 programme of study. They describe differences between the properties of different materials and explain how these differences are used to classify substances as solids, liquids and gases. They describe some methods, such as filtration, that are used to separate simple mixtures. They use scientific terms, such as evaporation or condensation, to describe changes. They use knowledge about some reversible and irreversible changes to make simple predictions about whether other changes are reversible or not.

TASK 5 — SOLIDS, LIQUIDS AND GASES A/B
C67 -68

Resources
Copymaster C67, examples of solids, liquids and gases (fizzy drinks), spoons, water, crayons, a balloon full of air.

Organization
This is a class lesson (it is expensive to conduct as a paired or individual investigation).

What you do
Discuss the characteristics of gases, liquids and solids – how do they differ? Give children copies of copymaster C67 and explain the tasks which are to draw particles of a solid, liquid and gas and say how they differ (the particles of a solid are closely packed together, those of a liquid less tightly packed whilst those of a gas as further apart still); to categorize common materials as solids, liquids or gases and describe their properties.

What the child does
The child draws diagrams to represent molecules in solids, liquids and gases, and completes copymaster C67.

Key questions
Do children know the characteristics of solids, gases and liquids? Can they classify materials as solids, gases or liquids and write about their properties?

Reassessment
Use copymaster C68, three cans of fizzy drinks and three cans, cartons or bottles of still drinks, an accurate balance, a clock.

TASK 6 — FILTRATION – SEPARATING MIXTURES A/B
C69 -70

Resources
Sand, gravel, filter funnel, jars, muddy water (soil and water mixed together), stop clock, copymaster C69.

Organization
The children work in pairs (monitor individual input).

What you do
Discuss the need for clean water and how dirty or muddy water can be purified and cleaned. Make a trip to a water purification plant (or look up in a book), to find out about the practical treatment of river water so that it is fit to drink. (Filtering water through sand and gravel beds to clean it.) Give out copies of copymaster C69 to each child and explain the tasks which are to use the equipment illustrated on the copymaster to design a simple filtering system to purify muddy water, and to suggest ways of improving the filtering design in order to make the water cleaner still (perhaps by adding a further stage in filtering or by using a different type of filter such as paper).

What the child does
The child places sand and gravel in layers into a filter funnel and pours muddy water on to gravel, times how long it takes for the water to pass through the filtering system, and catches the purified water in a jar. The child then modifies the layers of gravel and sand to try to optimize the process, and checks the filtered water, and to see if it is clean and refilters it if necessary. The child then writes an account of what happened, and completes all tasks on the copymaster.

Key question
Do children understand the process of filtration and the importance of clean water?

Reassessment
Use copymaster C70.

TASK 7 — EVAPORATION AND CONDENSATION A/B
C71 -72

Resources
Copymaster C71, kettle, cool plate, jar.

Organization
Each child works individually.

What you do
Give out copies of copymaster C71 and explain the tasks which are to explain what happens to the water in the kettle when it is heated and to draw a diagram to show what happens, to predict what will be seen on the cold plate as the kettle boils, and to complete the sentence on

the copymaster and give two more examples of evaporation and condensation. Perform a class demonstration because of the need for safety.

What the child does
The child explains what happens to a kettle of water when it is heated and the effect of the cold plate on the steam, and completes all tasks on the copymaster.

Key question
Can the child use the terms evaporation and condensation to describe accurately the changes that take place as the water is heated and the steam is cooled?

Reassessment
Use copymaster C72, water, a polythene bag big enough to go over a large bowl, a large bowl, a plant stick. The child investigates evaporation and condensation in a simplified water-cycle experiment and labels a diagram of the water cycle.

TASK 8
ARE CHANGES REVERSIBLE OR IRREVERSIBLE? A/B
C73 -74

Resources
Plaster of Paris, kettle with water, matches and a candle in a holder, a chocolate bar, an electric fire, copymaster C73.

Organization
The children work in groups or individually.

What you do
Talk about changes to materials that are irreversible and reversible. Demonstrate how the materials change: a match burning, candle wax melting, chocolate melting when held in hands, and how plaster changes from powder and water to a hard solid substance when mixed. Give out copies of copymaster C73 and explain the task which is to say whether the changes illustrated can be reversed or not and to explain why.

What the child does
The children complete copymaster C73.

Key question
Do the children know which changes are reversible and which are irreversible and can they explain why?

Reassessment
Use copymaster C74, a camping stove, ingredients for fairy cakes, hot water for melting jelly, matches and wood, ice-cubes, Back Ton oven clay (available from NES Arnold) and ceramic pots, jelly. The task on copymaster C74 is similar to that on C73 except that the teacher demonstrates how jelly changes from solid to liquid and to solid again, how clay changes into fired ceramics, and how cake ingredients change into cakes. The children then complete the copymaster.

LEVEL 5

Level Description

Pupils demonstrate an increasing knowledge and understanding of aspects of materials and their properties drawn from Key Stage 2 or Key Stage 3 programme of study. They describe some metallic properties, such as good electrical conductivity, and use these properties to distinguish metals from other solids. They identify a range of contexts in which changes, such as evaporation or condensation, take place. They use knowledge about how a specific mixture, such as salt and water, or sand and water, can be separated to suggest ways in which other similar mixtures might be separated.

TASK 9
METALLIC PROPERTIES A/B
C75 -76

Resources
Copymaster C75, wire, wire-cutters, bulbs and holders, batteries, crocodile clips, and materials to test: a pencil, a necklace, a potato, a crayon, glass, keys, and a large nail.

Organization
The children work individually or in pairs.

What you do
Encourage and help the children to set up and use a circuit that will test which materials conduct electricity (if the material is a conductor then the bulb will light up). Ask them how they will record their results. Give out copies of copymaster C75 and explain the tasks which are to

predict which of the given materials illustrated on the copymaster will conduct electricity, to select equipment to make a circuit to test the conductivity of the objects and to draw a circuit diagram on the copymaster, to test the predictions using the circuit and report the results. Ask the children to explain their findings.

What the child does
The children predict which of the given materials will conduct electricity, make an electrical circuit to test materials for conductivity, test each material, and record the results and write a conclusion.

Key questions
Can the children describe metallic properties? Can the children identify materials that allow the passage of electric current (conductors) and those that do not allow the passage of electric current (insulators). Can children recognize metals as electrical conductors?

Reassessment
Use copymaster C76, wire, wire-cutters, bulbs and holders, batteries, crocodile clips, and materials for testing: a metal spoon, a plastic spoon, a wooden spoon, a brass screw, a piece of Lego®, a slice of bread.

TASK 10 — SOME METALS ARE MAGNETIC A/B

C77 -78

Resources
Copymaster C77, a variety of magnets, and metals to test: paperclips, copper wire, keys, 5p coins and 2p coins, a cola can, washers, a ring and a metal hairclip.

Organization
The children work individually or in pairs.

What you do
Ask the children how they can determine which materials are magnetic. Give the children a copy of copymaster C77 and explain the task which is to predict which of the metallic objects are magnetic, to test their predictions, and to record the results and draw conclusions.

What the child does
The child predicts which of the metallic objects are magnetic, investigates to find out which materials are attracted to or repelled by magnets, records the results and reaches conclusions.

Key question
Can the children identify metallic properties? Can children describe magnetic properties?

Reassessment
Use copymaster C78, a big horse-shoe magnet, iron filings, safety pins, aluminium foil, a plastic comb, a paper fastener (bulldog clip), a pair of scissors, a metal safety rule.

TASK 11 — EVAPORATION A/B

C79 -80

Resources
Copymaster C79, three identical pieces of cloth, equal amounts of water with which to saturate the cloth samples, a stop clock, a freezer, a warm place and a cool place.

Organization
The children work individually or in pairs but monitor individual output.

What you do
Ask the children questions such as 'Where does the water go from the clothes on a washing line and why does this happen?' (eg water molecules turn to water vapour and more so at a higher temperature). Give out copies of copymaster C79 and explain the task which is to consider the illustrations on the copymaster that show three identical pieces of cloth saturated in water; one placed in a fridge, one on a hot radiator and the third in a cool cupboard; and to answer the questions on the copymaster. Encourage fair testing, recording of results and explanation of findings.

What the child does
The child saturates three equally sized pieces of identical cloth in water and places one piece in a fridge, one in a cool cupboard and the other on a hot radiator. The child regularly assesses the dampness of the samples and records the times taken for all three pieces of cloth to dry and draws a conclusion.

Key question
Can the children explain the best conditions for evaporation?

Reassessment
Use copymaster C80, 1000 ml water, a graduated 1 litre jug. The task is to explain and record the evaporation of water over a period of a week from a graduated jug containing 1000 ml of water placed directly in a sunny position.

TASK 12 — SEPARATING MIXTURES A/B

C81 -82

Resources
Sand, salt, iron filings, beakers, a funnel, filter paper, magnet (covered with paper), copymaster C81.

Organization
The children work in groups.

What you do
Give the children mixtures of sand and salt, salt and iron filings, salt and water, and sand and water and challenge them to separate them.

What the child does
The children choose equipment and methods for separation, separate the mixture of sand and salt, draw off the iron filings with a paper-covered magnet, pour the sand and water through a filter funnel, evaporate the water from the salt and water mixture, and record and explain the results.

Key question
Can the children use knowledge about specific mixtures to separate them?

Reassessment
Use copymaster C82, sugar, iron filings, fine gravel, a magnet, clear plastic containers, thin white paper, an electric ring, a saucepan, a filter funnel and filter paper.

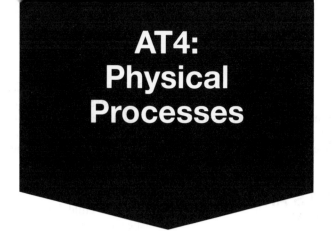

AT4:
Physical Processes

| LEVEL 2 | **Level Description** |

Pupils know about a range of physical phenomena and recognise and describe similarities and differences associated with them. They compare the way in which devices, such as bulbs, work in different electrical circuits. They compare the effects of similar phenomena, such as the brightness or colour of lights, or the loudness or pitch of sounds. They compare the movement of different objects in terms of speed or direction.

TASK 1 — COMPARING EFFECTS A/B
C83 -84

Resources
Red sunglasses (made from card and acetate), red pot, yellow flower, blue book, copymaster C83.

Organization
The children work in pairs.

What you do
Talk about the ways that colours can be changed by looking through coloured filters. Help the children make some red-coloured sunglasses from card and acetate (these can be decorated as part of a D & T activity). Give out copies of copymaster C83 and explain the task which is to paint the colours of the three objects seen through the red sunglasses and to compare these with the colours they see without the sunglasses.

What the child does
The child observes differences of colours of the same three objects, records accurately the colours they see with and without the red sunglasses, and discusses the changes.

Key question
Can the children observe how the colour of light may be altered? Do the children know that colours mix?

Reassessment
Use copymaster C84, blue sunglasses (made from card and acetate), a yellow T-shirt, a blue jug, a red balloon. The task on copymaster C84 is similar to that on C83 except using blue-coloured sunglasses instead of red ones.

| LEVEL 3 | **Level Description** |

Pupils use their knowledge and understanding to link cause and effect in simple explanations of physical phenomena, such as a bulb failing to light because of a break in an electrical circuit, or the direction or speed of movement of an object changing because of a force applied to it. They begin to make simple generalisations about physical phenomena, such as explaining that sounds they hear become fainter the further they are from the source.

TASK 2 — BREAKS IN CIRCUITS A/B
C85 -86

Resources
Copymaster C85, bulbs, wires, crocodile clips, batteries.

Organization
Each child works individually.

What you do
Give out copies of copymaster C85 and explain the task which is to examine the illustrations on the copymaster and to write down whether the bulb will light up in each case and explain why, and to test the answers by doing the experiments.

What the child does
The child writes down whether the bulb will light or not in the illustrated circuits and explains why, does the

experiments to check and reinforce their knowledge.

Key question
Does the child know why a bulb will not light and why it will light and can they explain the reasons (with the aid of diagrams if necessary)?

Reassessment
Use copymaster C86, bulbs, wires, crocodile clips, batteries. The task on copymaster C86 is similar to that on C85. Set up further practical investigations and use copymaster C86 again until the children perform the task satisfactorily.

TASK 3 — FORCES APPLIED TO OBJECTS A/B
C87 -88

Resources
Copymaster C87.

Organization
Each child works individually.

What you do
Give out copymaster C87 and explain the task which is to identify the forces acting in the illustrated situations, to show the forces using arrows, and to explain in writing what happens. Teachers can demonstrate some examples.

What the child does
The child explains where the forces are acting in the pictures on the copymaster by using arrows and written explanations.

Key question
Can the child explain how and why the speed or direction of an object changes when a force is applied to it?

Reassessment
Use copymaster C88.

TASK 4 — SOUNDS OVER DISTANCE A/B
C89 -90

Resources
Loud ticking clock, long, medium and short cardboard tubes, yoghurt pots, string, copymaster C89.

Organization
Each child works individually.

What you do
Discuss with the children how sound is dissipated the further from the sound source you are, and how sound can be transmitted through different materials. Give children copies of copymaster C89 and explain the task which is to carefully consider the illustrations, to tick the appropriate boxes, and to test and explain their choices. Make sure the children understand that the telephone will only work if the string is taut.

What the child does
The child completes the first task on the copymaster then checks the predictions by placing the clock at a short distance on a table and listening to it through a short tube, then places the clock at a longer distance on the table and listens to it through a medium-length tube. The child then repeats the test with a longer tube. The child completes the second task on the copymaster and uses the resources to check their knowledge by making a telephone from the resources provided by making a hole in the bottom of each yoghurt pot with a nail, knotting some string which is threaded through the holes in both pots and knotted again as shown in the diagram. The child tests the telephone by talking to another child with it, then makes other telephones with longer strings and observes the volume of sound in each telephone.

Key question
Can the child describe what happens to the sound when the source is moved further away? Does the child know about reflected sound (in the tube)? Can the child explain that the longer the distance between the yoghurt pots the fainter the sound will be?

Reassessment
Use copymaster C90. As further reassessment activities, try different investigations such as using iron railings to conduct sound.

LEVEL 4

Level Description

Pupils demonstrate knowledge and understanding of aspects of physical processes drawn from the Key Stage 2 or Key Stage 3 programme of study. They describe and explain physical phenomena, such as how a particular device in an electrical circuit may be switched on or off, or how the apparent position of the Sun changes over the course of a day. They make generalisations about physical phenomena, such as motion being affected by forces, including gravitational attraction, magnetic attraction and friction, or sounds being heard through a variety of materials. They use the idea that light travels to explain phenomena such as the formation of shadows.

TASK 5 — SWITCHES IN CIRCUITS A/B

C91 -92

Resources
Copymaster C91, electrical equipment: bulbs, buzzers, wire, batteries, crocodile clips, switches.

Organization
Each child works individually.

What you do
Give out copymaster C91 and explain the task which is to write down what will happen in each of the four circuits illustrated on the copymaster. Demonstrate the four circuits as a practical reinforcement.

What the child does
The child completes the tasks on the copymaster or as preparation for assessment follows the designs on the copymaster using the resources to investigate the circuits.

Key question
Does the child know circuits can be switched on and off?

Reassessment
Use copymaster C92, bulbs, buzzers, wire, batteries, crocodile clips, switches, scrap materials, tubes, yoghurt pots, paints, brushes, glues, Sellotape ®. The children design and draw circuit diagrams using a switch for either a flashing model lighthouse, a Morse code machine or a model with flashing eyes.

TASK 6 — THE SUN'S POSITION DURING THE DAY A/B

C93 -94

Resources
Copymaster C93.

Organization
Each child works individually.

What you do
On a sunny day take the children outside to observe what happens to the sun's apparent position and how shadows are formed throughout the day. Tell them to keep notes and make diagrams. Give out copies of copymaster C93

and explain the task which is to draw in the position of the sun on the three diagrams representing three different times of the day, and to draw a boy's shadow cast in the afternoon and at midday and explain how the two shadows will be different.

What the child does
The child draws in the position of the sun at the three different times and draws the position of the boy's shadow.

Key question
Are the children aware that the position of the sun changes during the day? Do they know why that happens?

Reassessment
Use copymaster C94. The children estimate the time from shadows formed by a stick in the ground, and use models of the earth and the sun, talk about compass points, the position of the sun in the sky and consider the southerly aspect of the sun for the UK. For further reassessment they can design and make a sundial.

TASK 7 — MAGNETIC FORCES A/B

C95 -96

Resources
Copymaster C95.

Organization
Each child works individually.

What you do
Give out copies of copymaster C95 and explain the task which is to explain how magnetic games work.

What the child does
The child explains how magnetic games work and suggests other games based on magnetism.

Key question
Do the children know that motion is affected by magnetic force?

Reassessment
Use copymaster C96, strong and weak magnets, pins, a magnetized pin, Plasticine ®, toy plastic cars, bowl of water, a cork float.

TASK 8 — MOTION AND GRAVITY A/B

C97-98

Resources
Similarly sized potatoes and fir-cones, copymaster C97.

Organization
The children work individually or in pairs.

What you do
Encourage predictions of which object will fall to the floor first when dropped simultaneously and ask why. Give out copymaster C97 and explain the tasks which are to predict whether a fir-cone or a similarly sized potato dropped from the same height will hit the floor first, and to predict whether a big and a very small potato dropped simultaneously from the same height will hit the floor at the same time or not, then to test the predictions. Ask them to consider what will happen if a feather was used instead of the fir-cone. Ensure fair testing and raise questions about the size of the potato and fir-cone. What does 'of equal size' mean? What is same height from the floor?

What the child does
The child makes predictions about the time taken for each object to fall to the floor when dropped simultaneously, records the predictions, tests their predictions, and records results and makes suggestions about improving the test.

Key question
Can the child explain how motion is affected by gravity?

Reassessment
Use copymaster C98. The tasks on copymaster C98 are similar to those on C97 except that children complete the tasks on the copymaster using arrows to indicate the forces acting on the objects and explain what happens in each case.

TASK 9 — FRICTION AFFECTS MOTION A/B

C99-100

Resources
Wood blocks, string, mass in a bag (a set of marbles of standard mass), four different surfaces (eg sandpaper, vinyl, corrugated card, fluffy fabric), a table, copymaster C99.

Organization
The children work individually or in groups.

What you do
Give children copymaster C99 and explain the task which is to predict which surface will require the largest number of marbles to be placed in the bag to start the wooden block moving and which surface needs the least number of marbles and to test what mass (how many marbles) is required to move the wooden block on each of the four surfaces, then to explain why the different surfaces pro-

duce different results. Encourage fair tests and suggest how to change the mass with marbles. Encourage the children to record their results in tabular form. Discuss the effect of the surfaces on the mass necessary to start the block moving.

What the child does
The child ties a wooden block with a length of string to a bag that contains a mass (marbles), places the wooden block on a series of surfaces (with the mass in a bag hanging over the edge of the table as illustrated), then adds marbles until the bag moves, and records the mass (number of marbles) needed to start the block moving on the different surfaces. The child records and explains which surface produces the most friction, which one the least, and uses appropriate words that describe the surfaces.

Key question
Do the children know that friction impedes motion?

Reassessment
Use copymaster C100, a gently inclined slope of about 1 metre length (check the incline first so that the marble runs different distances on each surface), various surfaces for covering the slope, marbles, a tape measure.

TASK 10 — LIGHT AND THE FORMATION OF SHADOWS A/B

C101-102

Resources
Copymaster C101.

Organization
Each child works individually.

What you do
Discuss how shadows are formed. Give the children copymaster C101 and explain the task which is to complete a drawing of a shadow cast on a wall explaining why this happens, to draw shadows formed by trees and to explain where shadows will be cast by the trees, and to say if shadows will be cast anywhere else.

What the child does
The child undertakes practical investigations into the formation of shadows (goes outside to observe where and how shadows are formed) and completes the tasks on the copymaster.

Key question
Can the child use the way that light travels to explain how shadows are formed?

Reassessment
Use copymaster C102. The task on copymaster C102 is similar to that on C101 except that instead of shadows on the school grounds children investigate solar eclipses using a Helios Orrery. As a further practical assessment activity they can design and make a shadow-puppet theatre.

Level Description

LEVEL 5

Pupils demonstrate an increasing knowledge and understanding of aspects of physical processes drawn from the Key Stage 2 or Key Stage 3 programme of study. They begin to apply ideas about physical processes to suggest a variety of ways to make changes, such as altering the current in a circuit or altering the pitch or loudness of a sound. They begin to use some abstract ideas in descriptions, such as forces being balanced when an object is stationary, or objects being seen when light from them enters the eye. They use models to explain effects that are caused by the movement of the Earth, such as the length of a day or year.

TASK 11 — ALTERING CURRENT IN CIRCUITS A/B
C103 -104

Resources
Copymaster C103, bulbs, batteries, wires, crocodile clips.

Organization
Each child works individually.

What you do
Give out copymaster C103 and explain the task which is to examine carefully the circuits before answering set questions on the copymaster about what will happen in the given circuits and why.

What the child does
The child answers the questions on the copymaster and may undertake the tasks on the copymaster in a practical way. The child makes up and tests the circuits making a careful record of the observations.

Key question
Does the child know that altering the flow of current in a circuit changes a bulb's brightness? Does the child know that changing circuits can alter a bulb's light output?

Reassessment
Use copymaster C104, bulbs, batteries, wires, crocodile clips.

TASK 12 — ALTERING PITCH AND LOUDNESS OF SOUND A/B
C105 -106

Resources
A variety of musical resources and instruments, elastic bands, boxes of different lengths (or pieces of wood of different lengths), same-sized jars, measuring jugs, wooden xylophone hammer or similar implement, copymaster C105.

Organization
The children work in small groups (monitor individual input).

What you do
Allow the children to experience a variety of instruments to reinforce their knowledge of how sounds are made by vibrating objects. Discuss how notes of different pitches are made on the guitar. Discuss and investigate how quiet and loud sounds are made. Give out copymaster C105 and explain the task which is to write down what kind of sound an elastic band will produce when it is stretched over a long box, a medium-sized box and a short box and plucked, then to draw in levels of water on diagrams of jam jars which will produce high-, medium- and low-pitched sounds when tapped.

What the child does
The child explores sounds made by plucking elastic bands stretched over different lengths of boxes and explores the different sound pitches made by fifferent levels of water in jam jars and completes copymaster C105.

Key question
Do the children know the correct terminology for describing sounds? Can the children explain how different pitches are produced?

Reassessment
Use copymaster C106.

TASK 13 — FORCES BALANCED ON STATIONARY OBJECTS A/B
C107 -108

Resources
Copymaster C107.

Organization
Each child works individually.

What you do
Give out copies of copymaster C107 and explain the task which is to describe using arrows and diagrams the forces acting in the situations illustrated on the copymaster, and to explain the forces that act on stationary objects.

What the child does
The child shows with arrows and notes where the forces are acting on the objects to keep them stationary.

Key question
Do children know that forces are balanced when an object is stationary?

Reassessment
Use copymaster C108.

SEEING OBJECTS A/B

Resources
Copymaster C109.

Organization
Each child works individually.

What you do
Give out copies of copymaster C109 and explain the task which is to describe using arrows the way a woman can read a newspaper under the light of a lamp and to draw a detailed diagram (cross-section) of the light entering an eye.

What the child does
The child uses arrows to indicate how the light is travelling to allow the woman to read the newspaper and draws a detailed diagram (cross-section) of the light entering an eye.

Key question
Does the child know that the newspaper can only be seen when light enters the eye? Does the child realise that light can be reflected?

Reassessment
Use copymaster C110. The task on copymaster C110 is similar to that on C109 except that instead of how a woman can read under the light of a lamp and a cross-section of the light entering an eye, the child draws a diagram to show the direction of light so that a driver can see the Cat's-eyes reflected by the headlamps on the car.

EFFECTS CAUSED BY THE EARTH MOVING A/B

Resources
Copymaster C111, models of the earth and the sun (a Helios Orrery is ideal).

Organization
Each child works individually.

What you do
Ask the children to use the models to understand what happens as the earth moves in relation to the sun. Give out copies of copymaster C111 and explain the task which is to explain, using diagrams, why it is hotter in the summer than in the winter in the UK, and to answer the questions on the copymaster.

What the child does
The child uses the models and diagrams of the sun and the earth to investigate and explain why in summertime, Britain gets long days and short nights, and completes copymaster C111.

Key question
Can the child explain the differences between day and night, day length and year length in terms of the movement of the earth round the sun? Can the child explain how the tilt of the earth affects day and night lengths and the amount of light received by various geographical locations throughout the year?

Reassessment
Use copymaster C112, models of the earth on its axis, the moon and the sun. The task on copymaster C112 is similar to that on C111 except that the child investigates the position of the moon and the sun in relation to the earth, using models.

Name: _____ Date: _____

| A | Responding and predicting

Mixing colours

The names of the mixed colours could be:

purple   brown   green   mauve   orange   turquoise

Look at the pictures

Predict the colours that will be made in each case
Test your predictions

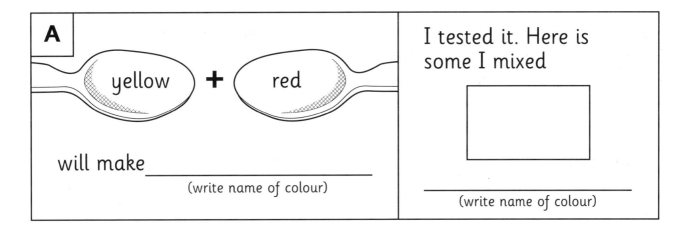

A yellow + red

will make _____
(write name of colour)

I tested it. Here is some I mixed

_____
(write name of colour)

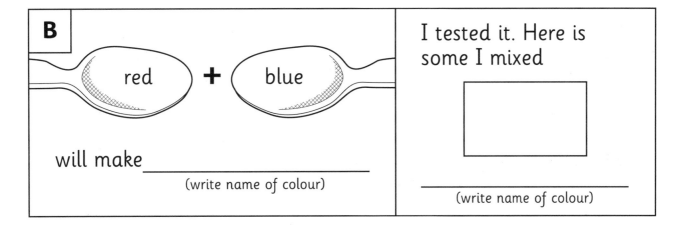

B red + blue

will make _____
(write name of colour)

I tested it. Here is some I mixed

_____
(write name of colour)

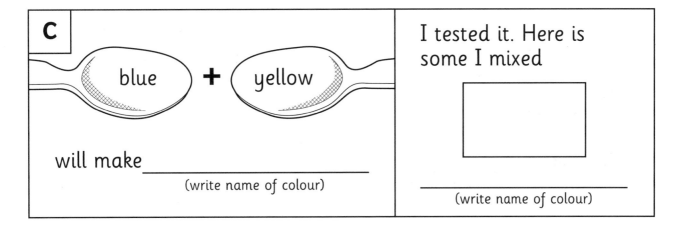

C blue + yellow

will make _____
(write name of colour)

I tested it. Here is some I mixed

_____
(write name of colour)

Name: _____ Date: _____

B | Responding and predicting

C2

Mixing colours

The names of the mixed colours could be:

purple   brown   green   mauve   orange   turquoise

Look at the pictures

Predict the colours that will be made in each case

Test your predictions

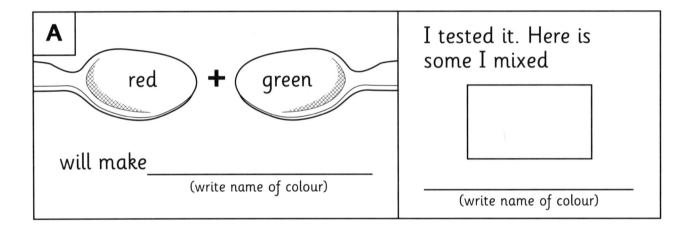

A

red + green

will make _____
(write name of colour)

I tested it. Here is some I mixed

_____
(write name of colour)

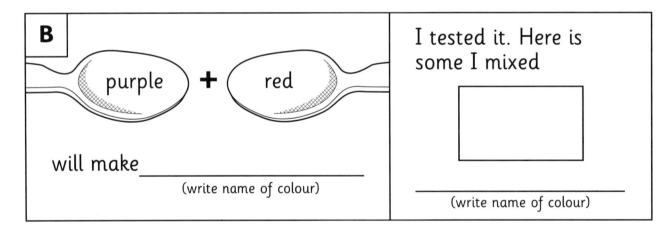

B

purple + red

will make _____
(write name of colour)

I tested it. Here is some I mixed

_____
(write name of colour)

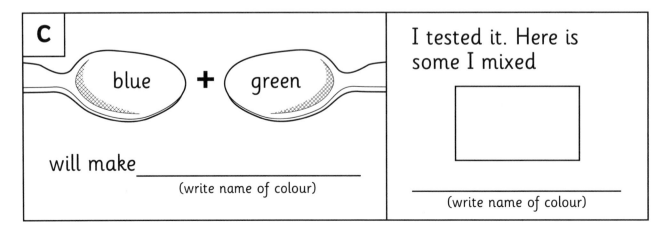

C

blue + green

will make _____
(write name of colour)

I tested it. Here is some I mixed

_____
(write name of colour)

A | Describe and record observations

C3

Predict which ones will float and which will sink

Join them to the correct bowl

ping-pong ball

stone

cork

piece of wood

piece of Plasticine

will float

will sink

piece of card

pencil

nail

orange

Lego brick

Now test them and record your results here by drawing pictures

sank					
floated					

How many did you get right?

I predicted _____ out of ten

Name: _____ Date: _____

B | Describe and record observations   C4

Predict which ones will float and which will sink

Join them to the correct bowl

tennis ball

jam jar lid

fir-cone

plastic animal

small empty pill bottle (with lid)

will float

will sink

small metal car

key

felt-tip pen

apple

screw

Now test them and record your results here by drawing pictures

sank						
floated						

How many did you get right?

I predicted _____ out of ten

Name: _____ Date: _____

| A | Answer questions, make predictions | C5 |

Which do you think will melt in your fingers?
Circle those which will

chocolate   apple   pasta (dry)

What do you think will happen if we put wax in a pan on the cooker?
Why?

wax	what will happen?
gentle heat	_____ _____ _____ _____ _____

Which will melt first, jelly or wax? _____

How do you know this? _____

_____

_____

Can chocolate become solid again once melted?

Circle your answer   **yes**   **no**

B | Answer questions, make predictions

C6

Which do you think will melt in your fingers?
Circle those which will

butter

rice

jelly

cheese

biscuit

carrot

chocolate

What do you think will happen if we put jelly in a pan on the cooker?
Why?

| jelly

gentle heat	**what will happen?**
	_____
	_____
	_____
	_____
	_____

Which will melt first, jelly or wax? _____

How do you know this? _____

_____

_____

Can wax become solid again once melted?

Circle your answer   **yes**   **no**

Name: _____ Date: _____

A | Fair test using simple equipment

C7 ▷

Will a bean germinate and grow with or without water?

Tick ✓ your choice (you can tick both if you want to)

The bean will germinate with water ☐

The bean will germinate without water ☐

Devise a fair test to find out and circle the things you will need

ruler	pots	syringe	soil	scales	sunlight	labels	thermometer	water

Draw a picture of your experiment (show both beans)
Label it carefully

Record the growth of the beans

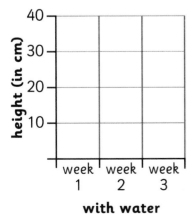

with water

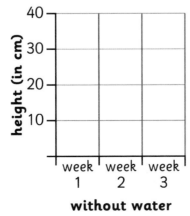

without water

Can you say how your test was fair? _____

_____

_____

_____

_____

_____

_____

B Fair test using simple equipment

C8

Will a bean germinate and grow with or without soil?

Tick ✓ your choice (you can tick both if you want to)

The bean will germinate and grow better with soil ☐

The bean will germinate and grow better without soil ☐

Devise a fair test to find out and circle the things you will need

ruler	pots	syringe	soil	scales	sunlight	labels	thermometer	water

Draw a picture of your experiment (show both beans)
Label it carefully

Record the growth of the beans

Can you say how your test was fair?

_____

_____

_____

_____

_____

_____

_____

_____

_____

with soil   **without soil**

Name: _____ Date: _____

A ‖ Measure, notice patterns, make report

**Start your investigation with two sets of
freshly sprouted cress seeds**

Stop watering one set but water the other set normally

Make drawings of each set of plants after one week

A with water	B without water

Draw a chart of how the cress grew, with and without water

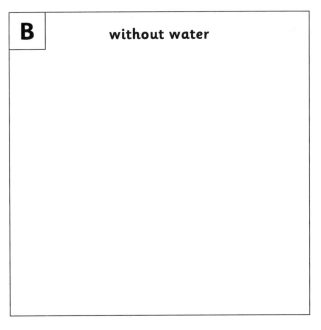

		Monday		Tuesday		Wednesday		Thursday		Friday	
		A	B	A	B	A	B	A	B	A	B

height (in mm): 25, 20, 15, 10, 5

What do you notice? _____

_____

_____

B │ Measure, notice patterns, make report C10 ▷

Start your investigation with two sets of freshly sprouted cress seeds

Put one set in a dark cupboard, keep the other in sunlight

Make drawings of each set of plants after one week

A with sunlight	B without sunlight

Draw a chart of how the cress grew, with and without sunlight

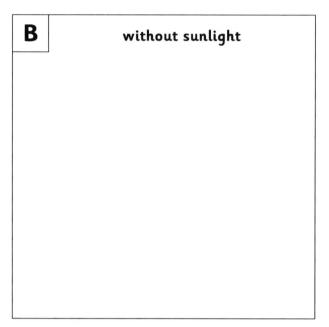

What do you notice? _____

_____

_____

Name: _____ Date: _____

A | Fair test varying one factor (1)

Teeth and sugar

What will you test? _____

_____

What do you think will happen? _____

_____

It is a fair test because _____

_____

Put teeth into four glasses, one containing pure water, the others containing soft drinks (three different brands)

Write down what is in each glass

A	pure water	B		C		D	

Draw diagrams (with notes) of the four after a week

A	pure water	B		C		D	

Name: _____ Date: _____

| B | Fair test varying one factor (1) | |

Teeth and sugar

What will you test? _____

_____

What do you think will happen? _____

_____

It is a fair test because _____

_____

Put teeth into four glasses, one containing black coffee only, one containing black coffee and one sugar, one containing black coffee and three sugars, and one containing black coffee and six sugars

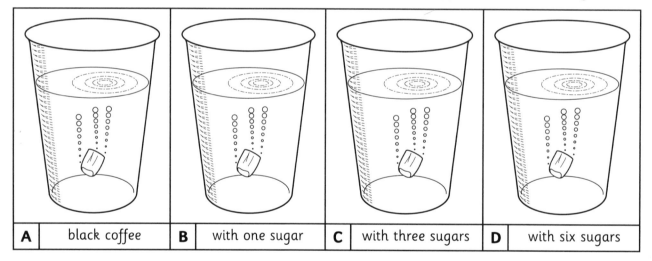

| A | black coffee | B | with one sugar | C | with three sugars | D | with six sugars |

Draw diagrams (with notes) of the four after a week

| A | black coffee | B | with one sugar | C | with three sugars | D | with six sugars |

A | Fair test varying one factor (2)

The task is to set up a fair test

An iron nail, a piece of plastic, a pebble and a piece of copper are to be immersed in water, as in the picture, for a week

iron nail   plastic   pebble   copper

How will you ensure that the test is fair? _____

_____

_____

How do you think each one will look after a week in water?

The nail will look _____

The plastic will look _____

The pebble will look _____

The copper will look _____

After a week, have any changed?

If so, say what has happened and draw a picture to show the changes

_____

_____

_____

_____

_____

_____

Name: _____ Date: _____

B ‖ Fair test varying one factor (2)

The task is to set up a fair test
Three iron nails are to be kept for a week

a
iron nail completely dry

b
iron nail after dipping in water

c
iron nail immersed in water

How will you ensure that the test is fair? _____
_____
_____

How do you think each one will look after a week?
Nail **a** will look _____

Nail **b** will look _____

Nail **c** will look _____

What do you notice after a week?
Draw diagrams to show what you mean

_____
_____
_____
_____
_____
_____
_____
_____

Name: _____ Date: _____

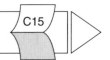

A │ Graphs, patterns and trends

Make a list of all your classmates
Record their hand spans and the length of their feet

Plot this data below. Put a small cross in the appropriate boxes
(one to show each person)

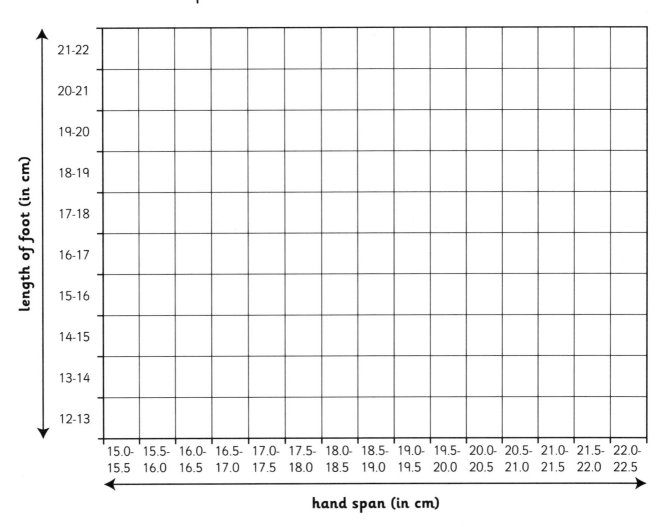

Can you see any patterns in the graph?   yes ☐   no ☐

If yes, what do you think the pattern means? _____

_____

_____

_____

_____

Name: _____ Date: _____

B **Graphs, patterns and trends**

For every member of your class plot the eye and hair colour on the graph below

(Place a small cross ✗ for each child in the appropriate box)
Label the axes

Hair colour	blue	green	honey	brown	black/ dark brown
black					
dark brown					
light brown					
red/ ginger					
blond					

Eye colour

Do you notice a pattern?   yes ☐   no ☐

If yes, what is it? What does it mean? _____

_____

Name: _____ Date: _____

| A | Use knowledge, make predictions | 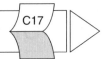 C17 |

Look at the diagrams

Each saucepan contains 20 grams of butter

What do you think would happen? Why?

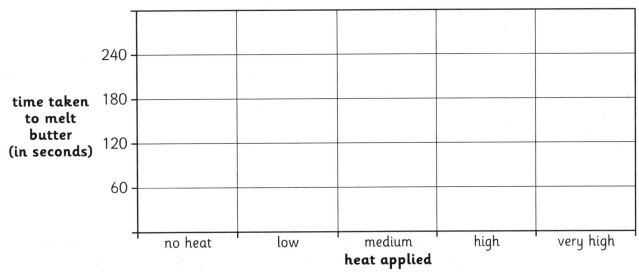

| no heat | low heat | medium heat | high heat | very high heat |

_____

_____

Which will melt first? Why? _____

_____

Test your predictions. Time and record your results here

time taken to melt butter (in seconds)

240 —
180 —
120 —
60 —

no heat   low   medium   high   very high

heat applied

Is this what you expected? _____

_____

B	Use knowledge, make predictions

Look at the diagrams
Each saucepan contains 20 grams of butter
What do you think would happen? Why?

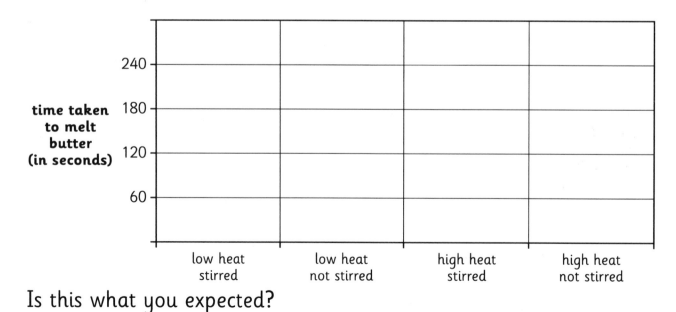

_____

_____

Which will melt first? Why? _____

_____

Test your predictions. Time and record your results here

Is this what you expected? _____

_____

_____

Name: _____ Date: _____

A | Identify key factors

C19

Look at the pictures
Circle the key factors

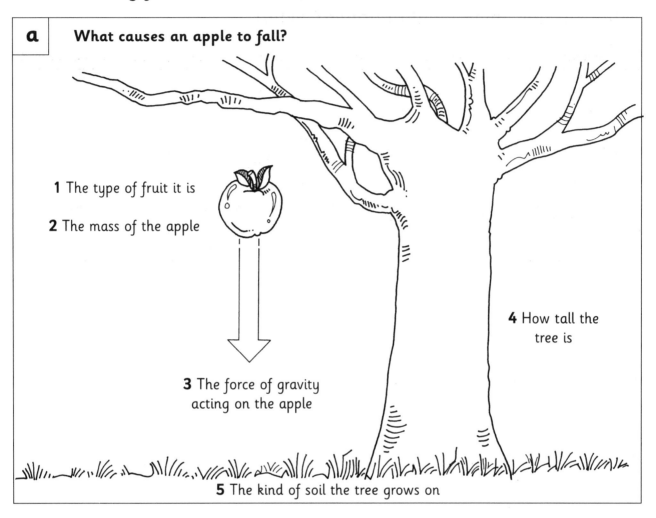

a **What causes an apple to fall?**

1 The type of fruit it is

2 The mass of the apple

3 The force of gravity acting on the apple

4 How tall the tree is

5 The kind of soil the tree grows on

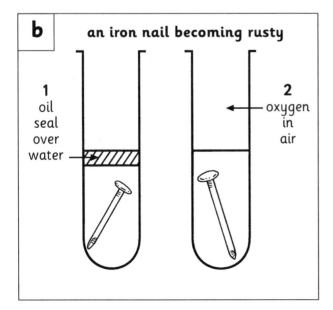

b **an iron nail becoming rusty**

1 oil seal over water

2 oxygen in air

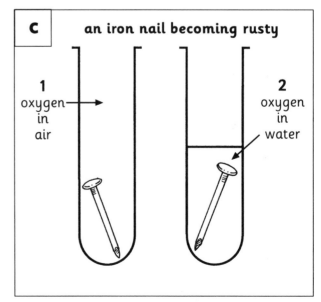

c **an iron nail becoming rusty**

1 oxygen in air

2 oxygen in water

Discuss the reasons for your choices

Name: _____ Date: _____

C20

B Identify key factors

Join the key factors to the pictures
(some key factors may be used more than once)

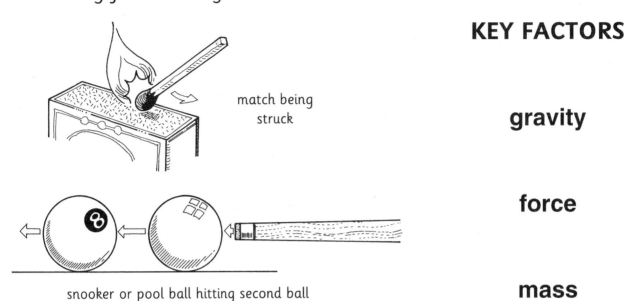

match being
struck

snooker or pool ball hitting second ball

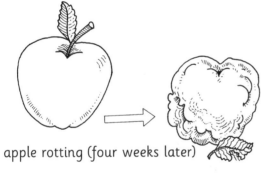

apple rotting (four weeks later)

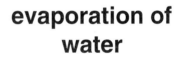

bread being
toasted

ice cube melted

KEY FACTORS

gravity

force

mass

**evaporation of
water**

heat

friction

**chemical
changes**

**transfer of
energy**

Discuss the reasons for your choice

A | Repeated observations, line graphs

C21

The diagram shows a ping-pong ball bouncing three times

Explain what happens _____

_____

_____

_____

_____

_____

_____

_____

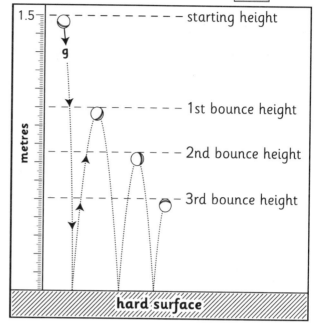

Choose and set up equipment carefully
Measure accurately the three bounce heights (measure each separately). Do the test three times. Record your results here:

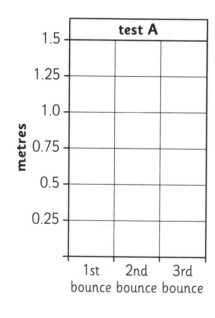

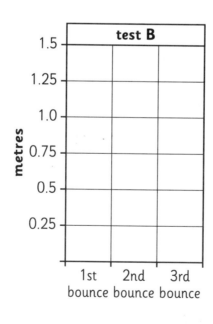

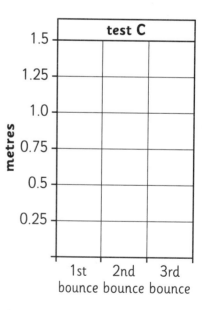

Are the results of all three tests identical? If not, why not?

_____

_____

_____

_____

Name: _____ Date: _____

| B | Repeated observations, line graphs | C22 |

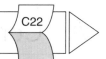

Drop a tennis ball from 1.5 metres on to three different surfaces: concrete, wood and grass

Record the results below (do the test three times)

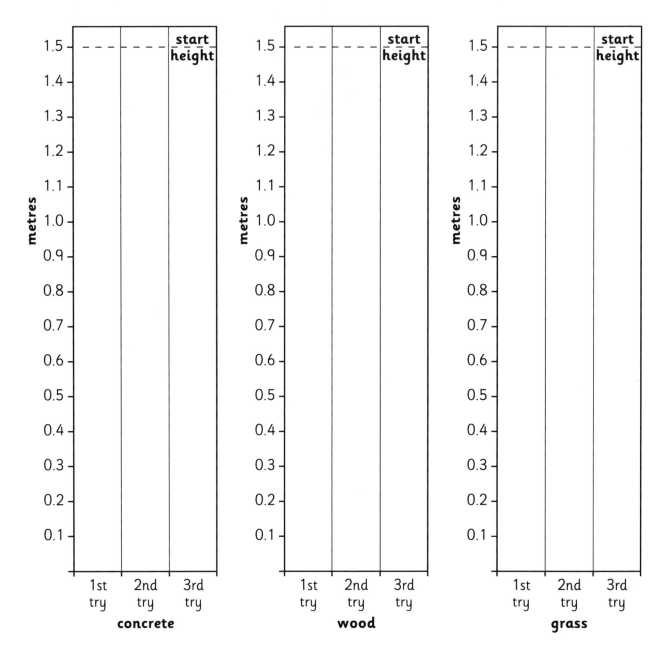

Can you explain differences between:
a bounces on different surfaces   **b** bounces on the same surface

_____

_____

_____

_____

Name: _____ Date: _____

| A | Conditions for plant growth | C23 |

Look at the pictures
All the beans are warm and watered correctly

1 in total darkness   **2** in full sunlight   **3** in a box with only
                                                                    one side open

How will each one grow?
1
_____

2
_____

3
_____

Say what happened
1
_____

_____

2
_____

_____

3
_____

_____

Name: _____ Date: _____

B | Conditions for plant growth

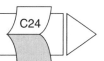

C24

Look at the pictures
All the bean plants are warm and in sunlight

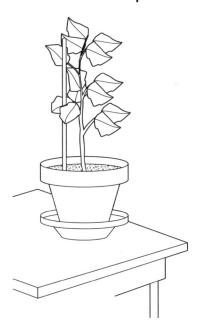

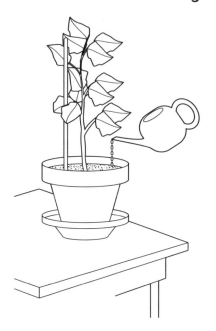

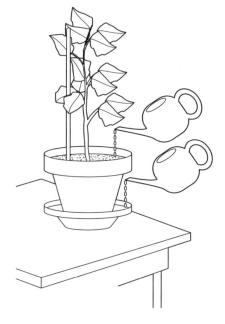

1 without water

2 watered when soil dry

3 kept in saturated soil at all times

How will each one grow?

1 _____

2 _____

3 _____

Say what happened

1 _____

_____

2 _____

_____

3 _____

_____

Name: _____ Date: _____

A | Animal life processes

snake

camel

tortoise

chimpanzee

cat

gymnast

fish

Which things do all the animals need?

Tick ✓ choices

food ☐	exercise ☐	books ☐	warmth ☐
air ☐	water ☐	toys ☐	shelter ☐
friends ☐	tv ☐	light ☐	care ☐

B | Animal life processes

C26

Draw your favourite pet here

What does your pet need to be healthy? _____

_____

_____

_____

_____

_____

_____

_____

_____

_____

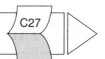

A | Living things and their homes   C27

Match the plant with its home

pot plant

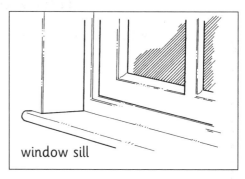
window sill

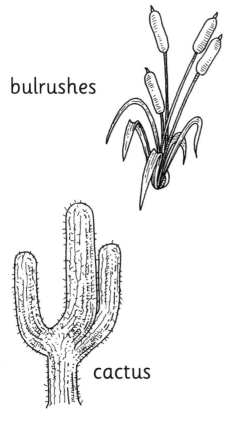
bulrushes

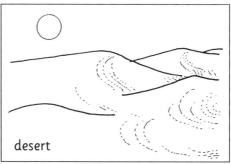
desert

cactus

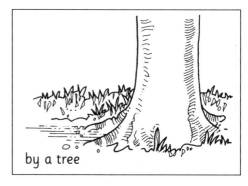
by a tree

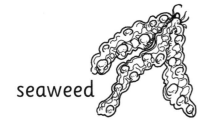
seaweed

in a river

mushrooms

under the sea

Explain the reasons for your choices

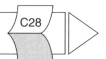

B │ Living things and their homes

Match the animal with its home

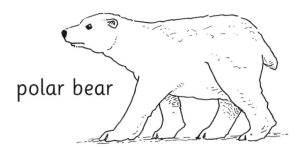

polar bear

in the sea

dragonfly

in the rain forest

starfish

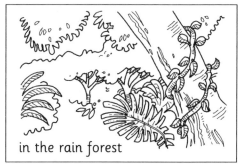

by a river

woodlouse

in the snow

parrot

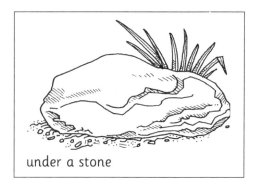

under a stone

Explain the reasons for your choices

Name: _____ Date: _____

A │ Animal and plant groups

C29

hedgehog

eagle

jay

penguin

zebra

squirrel

chimpanzee

panda

kingfisher

| **birds** | **mammals** |

Join the labels to the correct pictures

Can you name two more mammals and two more birds?

_____

_____

Birds are different from mammals because _____

_____

_____

_____

B | Animal and plant groups

Draw a red circle round all the fungi
Draw a blue circle round all the ferns
Draw a green circle round all the flowering plants

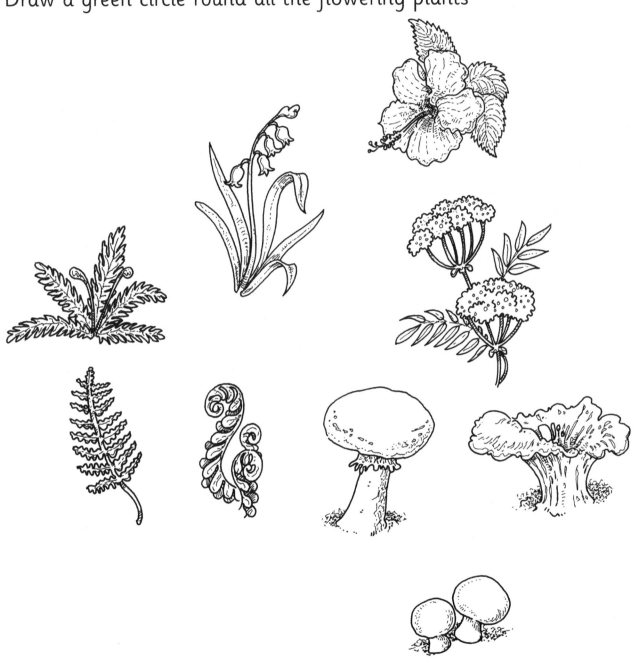

How are ferns and flowering plants different?

_____

_____

_____

_____

_____

Name: _____ Date: _____

A ‖ Reproduction

Cut out the pictures
Stick mothers and babies together

fish

tadpole

dog

butterfly

eggs under leaf

cat

mother

kitten

frog

puppy

calf

cow

fry

baby

B │ Reproduction

Look in books to find the mothers
Draw them next to their babies here
Name them

Tadpole and _____

Kitten and _____

Eggs under leaf and _____

Calf and _____

A | Living and non-living things

Analyse the front page of a newspaper
Sort and list into these two columns

living things	non-living things

What do all living things have in common?
Colour the petals of the daisies with these things

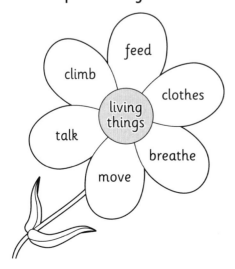

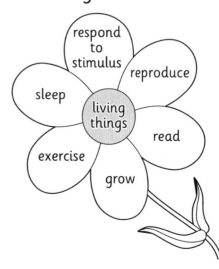

B Living and non-living things

C34

What do we need to grow?
Circle your choices

water

air

exercise

sleep

warmth

food

football

tv

reading

In which ways are living and non-living things different?

_____

_____

_____

Draw and name two non-living things

name _____

name _____

Name: _____ Date: _____

A | Suitable animal homes

Identify ways in which these animals are suited to
the environment in which they live

fish	
chicks	
frog	
rabbit	
polar bear	
stick insect	

B Suitable animal homes

C36

Identify ways in which these animals are suited to
the environment in which they live

leopard chasing prey	
hippo wallowing	
dog in kennel	
husky pulling sled	
whale spouting	
camel in desert	

Name: _____ Date: _____

| A | Name and position human organs |

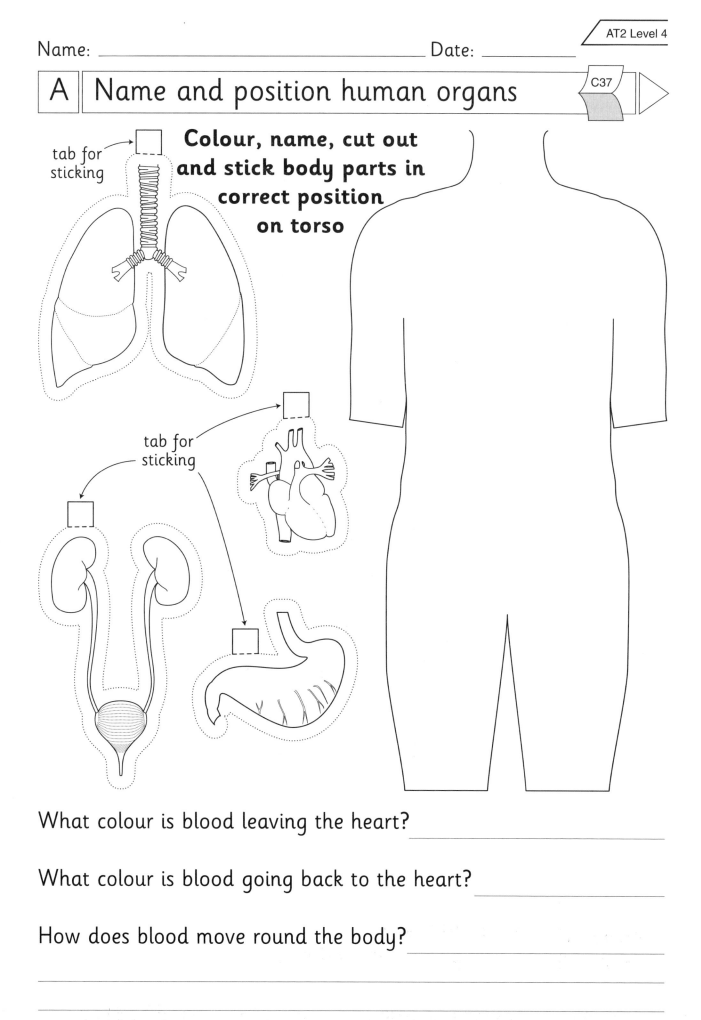

tab for sticking

Colour, name, cut out and stick body parts in correct position on torso

tab for sticking

tab for sticking

What colour is blood leaving the heart? _____

What colour is blood going back to the heart? _____

How does blood move round the body? _____

_____

_____

_____

Name: _____ Date: _____

B │ Name and position human organs

C38

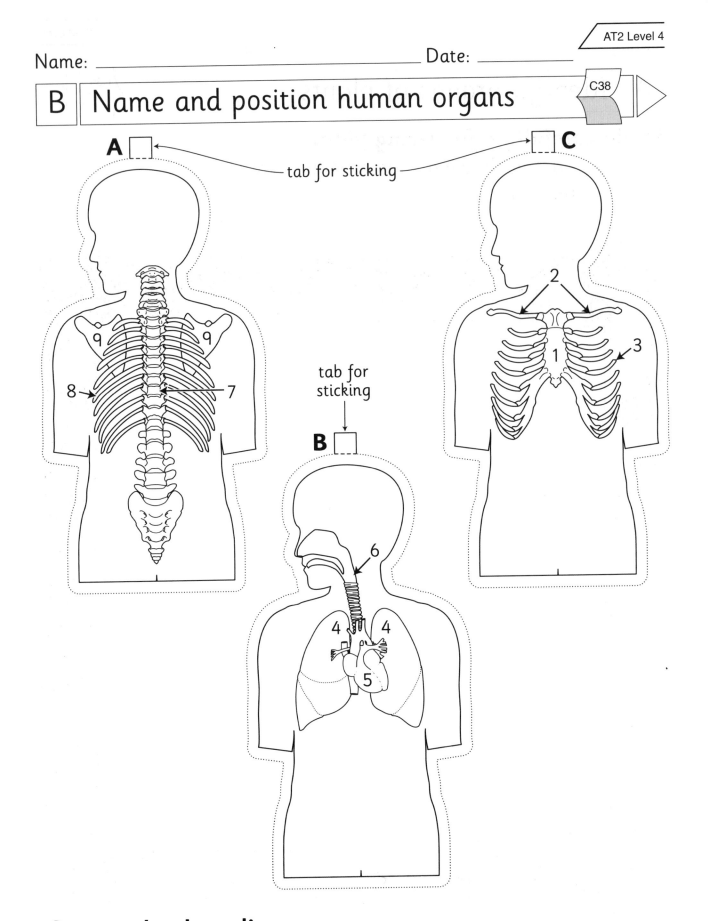

A ☐ ← tab for sticking → ☐ C

tab for sticking

B ☐

Cut out the three diagrams
Use the tabs to stick **B** on to **A**, and **C** on to **B**

Stick the completed model on to a fresh piece of paper
The numbered parts should be named under the completed model

| A | Identify organs of plants |

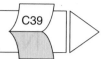

C39

Study carefully a flowering plant
Draw it in detail showing stigma, style, ovary,
stamen, stem and petal
Label the flower parts

My flower is _____

Colour the parts carefully and accurately

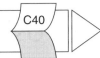
B	Identify organs of plants

C40

Label the flower parts

petal, stigma, anther, filament, ovary, pedicel, sepal, ovule and receptacle

Name: _____ Date: _____

A | Use keys to group living things
C41

Sarah has four different plants

a

b

c

d

She has made a key
to identify them.
Use the key and
write down the
plant names.

Is it a vegetable?

Yes — Does it grow under the earth?

No — Is it a flower?

Does it grow under the earth?
Yes — Carrot
No — Bean

Is it a flower?
No — Tree
Yes — Does it have thorns?

Does it have thorns?
Yes — Rose
No — Daffodil

Name the plants

a _____

b _____

c _____

d _____

B | Use keys to group living things

Collect six minibeasts
Draw and name them here (use books to help you)

a	b	c
name _____	name _____	name _____

d	e	f
name _____	name _____	name _____

How are they different? Tick ✓ boxes

minibeast	has legs	has 6 legs	has wings	has hard body	is flexible	can swim	has spots	walks	wriggles	hops	slides
a											
b											
c											
d											
e											
f											

Construct a simple key so that you, or someone else, can quickly identify them

Name: _____ Date: _____

A │ Food chains

Look at the drawings

Draw arrows to show the food chains, ending at the top of
the chain

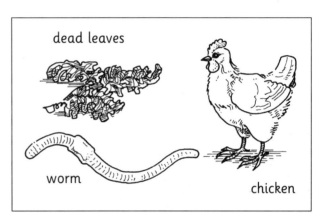

Make up your own food chain and illustrate it imaginatively

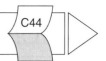
B Food chains

Cut out the pictures in each set and make three food chains by gluing and colouring
Identify the predator and prey in each chain

lettuce

blackbird

cat

snail

a

sheep

grass

human

lion

b

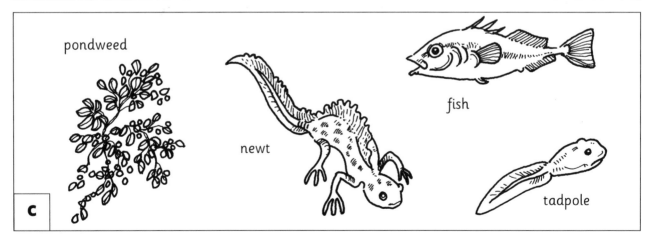

pondweed

newt

fish

tadpole

c

Do all food chains start with a green plant?_____

On a separate piece of paper make up your own food chain for living things found in the school ground. Illustrate the food chain.

Name: _____ Date: _____

A | Changes in living things – diet

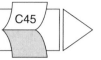

C45

Write down your daily menu, listing the vitamins, proteins, fats and carbohydrates in the meals – use reference books to help you

meal	My daily menu				
	food type	protein	carbohydrate	fat	vitamins and minerals
breakfast					
lunch					
dinner					
supper					
snacks					

Why I need a balanced diet _____

_____

_____

_____

| B | Changes in living things – diet |

C46

Use books to find out the four main food groups

Draw some sources for each – label them underneath

_____   _____

_____   _____

Complete the sentences

Proteins help to _____

_____

Fats give us _____

_____

Carbohydrates are used by our bodies for _____

_____

We need vitamins and minerals for _____

_____

On a separate piece of paper design a daily menu for an athlete. Do they need sugar? If so, why?

Name: _____ Date: _____

| A | Functions of human organs | 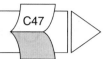 |

Can you explain what job these organs do?
You can use arrows on the diagrams to help you

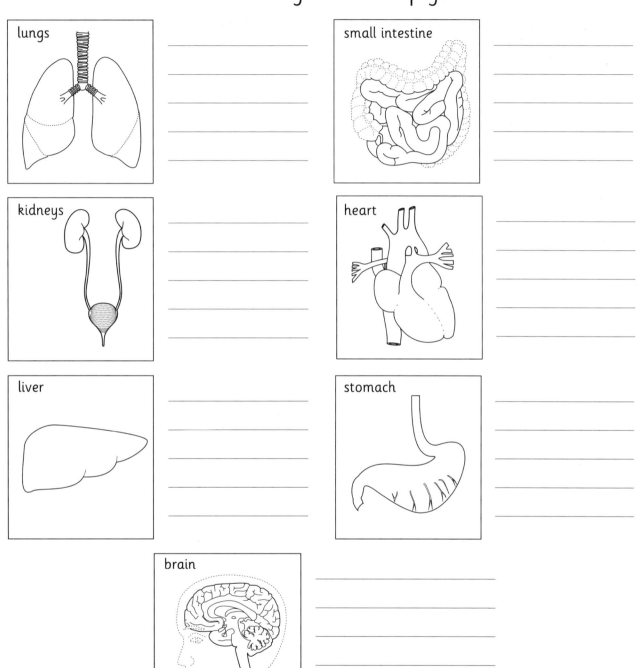

lungs
_____
_____
_____
_____

small intestine
_____
_____
_____
_____

kidneys
_____
_____
_____
_____

heart
_____
_____
_____
_____

liver
_____
_____
_____
_____

stomach
_____
_____
_____
_____

brain
_____
_____
_____
_____

What happens if the heart and lungs do not work properly?

_____

_____

_____

B | Functions of human organs

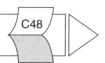

C48

Identify the heart, lungs, liver kidneys, intestines, stomach

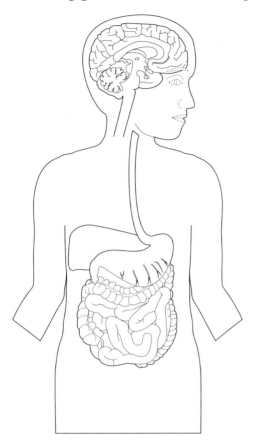

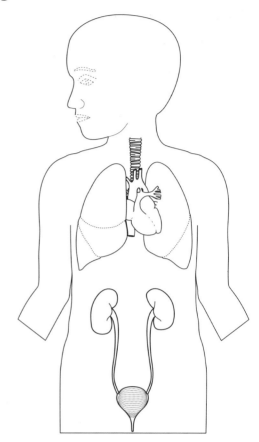

Describe the main function of these organs

heart _____

lungs _____

liver _____

kidneys _____

intestines _____

brain _____

stomach _____

Name: _____ Date: _____

A Functions of flowering plant organs

Take a flower that is ideal for insect pollination
Look at a section through the main organs
Using a magnifying glass, draw, colour and label the main organs
used in insect pollination

My drawing of a section through a flower

What is the function of each of these organs in insect pollination?

_____

_____

_____

Name: _____ Date: _____

B │ Functions of flowering plant organs

C50

Look at this drawing of a flowering plant, and label and name the sepals, petals, stigma, style, ovary, filament, anther – and anything else you can name

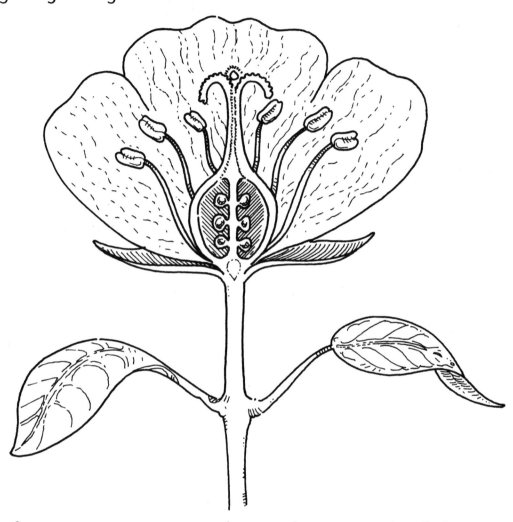

Write a few sentences to say what is the main job of the main organs and how they work in insect pollination

_____

_____

_____

_____

_____

_____

_____

_____

A | Human life cycle

Name the different stages in the female life cycle
(next to the pictures below)

_____

_____

_____

_____

_____   _____

Join the pictures (above) with arrows to produce the correct
time-line sequence

Describe the different stages of life _____

_____

_____

_____

_____

Is the life cycle of a female human similar to that of
a flowering plant? _____

_____

_____

Name: _____ Date: _____

| B | Human life cycle |

Name the different stages in the male life cycle
(next to the pictures below)

_____   _____

_____

_____   _____   _____

Join the pictures (above) with arrows to produce the correct
time-line sequence

Describe the different stages of life _____

_____

_____

_____

_____

_____

Is the life cycle of a male human similar to that of
a flowering plant? _____

_____

_____

Name: _____ Date: _____

A | Life cycles of plants

C53

How are these seeds dispersed?

seed/fruit	method of dispersal
coconut	
dandelion	
sycamore	
raspberry	
cherry	
strawberry	

How are these plants pollinated?

coconut _____

dandelion _____

sycamore _____

raspberry _____

cherry _____

strawberry _____

Name: _____ Date: _____

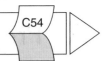

B | Life cycles of plants

C54

How are these seeds dispersed?

seed/fruit		method of dispersal
conker		
apple		
blackberry		
grass		
holly		
oak		

Draw arrows to show the way the seeds grow into flowering plants

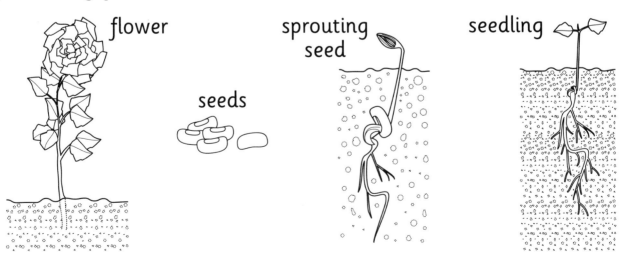

flower

seeds

sprouting seed

seedling

Name: _____ Date: _____

A │ Preferred habitats

C55

Collect some woodlice from the school grounds

Use a magnifying
glass and draw
one here ⟹

Can you devise a test
to find out which of these

| **damp and dark** |
| **dry and light** |

habitats is preferred by
woodlice?

Make a diagram of your experiment to find out which condition
woodlice prefer (What will you measure? How?)

What were your results?

_____

_____

_____

_____

_____

Can you make a table
or bar chart?

B Preferred habitats

Choose two habitats in the school grounds
(pond, under logs or bark chips)

What do you think might live in them?

In _____ **(a)** I think I will find _____

_____

In _____ **(b)** I think I will find _____

_____

Now go into the school grounds
Find out and record what does live in your two chosen habitats

creatures found in habitat **(a)**	I think they live there because . . .
creatures found in habitat (b)	**I think they live there because . . .**

Do any creatures inhabit both habitat **(a)** and **(b)**?
Which ones? Why do you think they do? _____

_____

Name: _____ Date: _____

A Classification of living things

Use these labels to classify all the animals on this page

mollusc	arachnid	insect
fish	amphibian	crustacean
mammal	reptile	bird

| B | Classification of living things |

Sort these into two groups, animals and plants

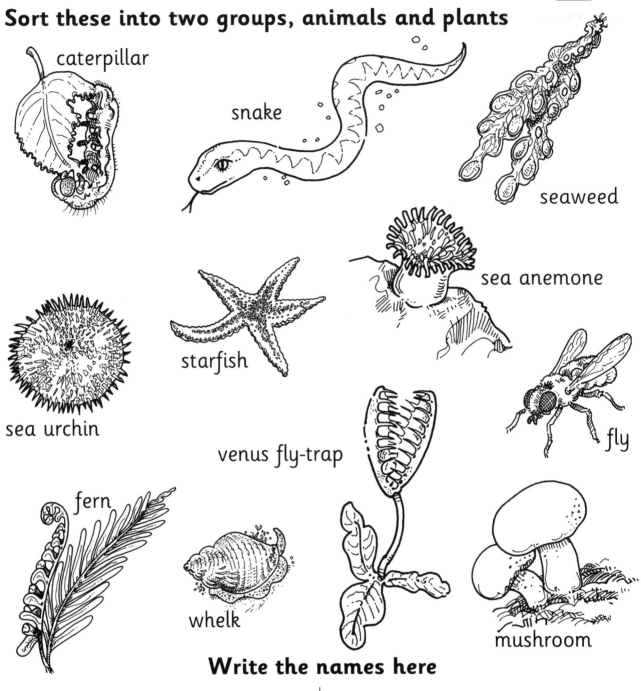

caterpillar

snake

seaweed

sea anemone

starfish

sea urchin

venus fly-trap

fly

fern

whelk

mushroom

Write the names here

animals	plants

Name: _____ Date: _____

A | Identifing common materials

Link the pictures to the words

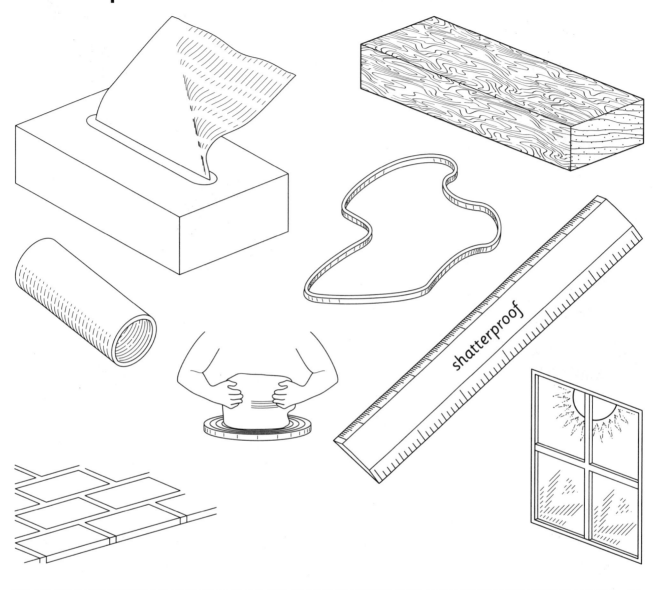

balsa wood	tissue-paper	rubber band	copper tubing	clay	concrete slab	plastic ruler	sheet of glass

Arrange the materials into two groups:

rigid	flexible
_____	_____
_____	_____
_____	_____
_____	_____

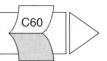
B | Identifying common materials

Draw a line to join the objects to the right descriptions

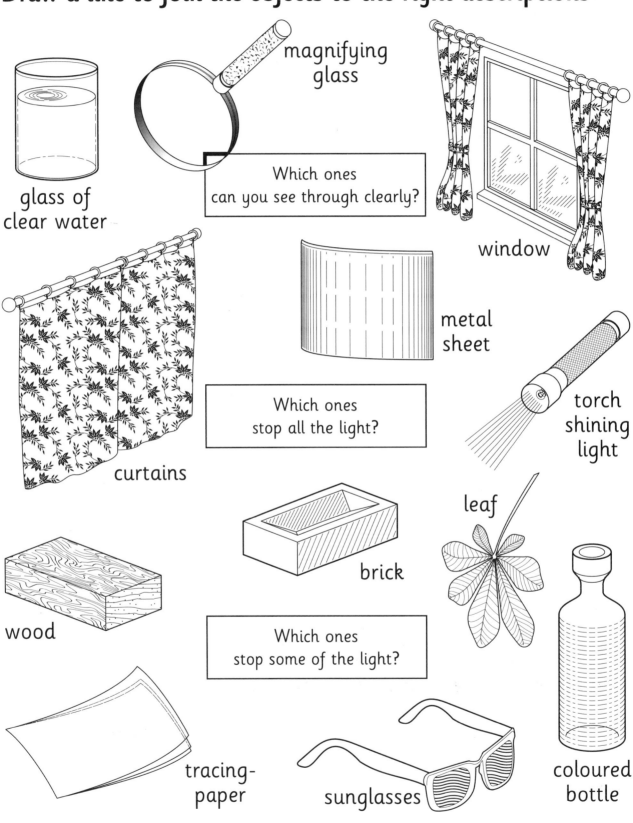

glass of
clear water

magnifying
glass

Which ones
can you see through clearly?

window

metal
sheet

curtains

Which ones
stop all the light?

torch
shining
light

leaf

wood

brick

Which ones
stop some of the light?

coloured
bottle

tracing-
paper

sunglasses

What does transparent mean? _____

Name: _____ Date: _____

A │ Material properties

What are these kitchen utensils made from?
Why are the materials suitable?

utensil	materials used	materials suitable because . . .
a		
b		
c		
d		
e		

Sort these into sets, according to the materials they are made
from. Write the letters in place.

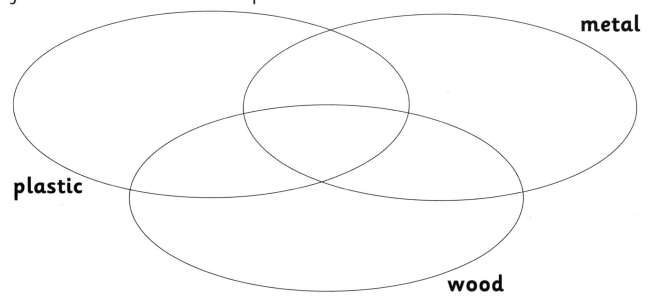

Name: _____ Date: _____

B ║ Material properties

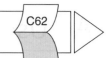

Look at the clothes on the washing line

woollen jumper

plastic placemat

cotton dress

silk scarf

linen pillow cover

nylon shirt

polyester trousers

Cut out the clothes and the labels and put them in the correct baskets

Cut along dotted lines so that clothes can be put in the baskets

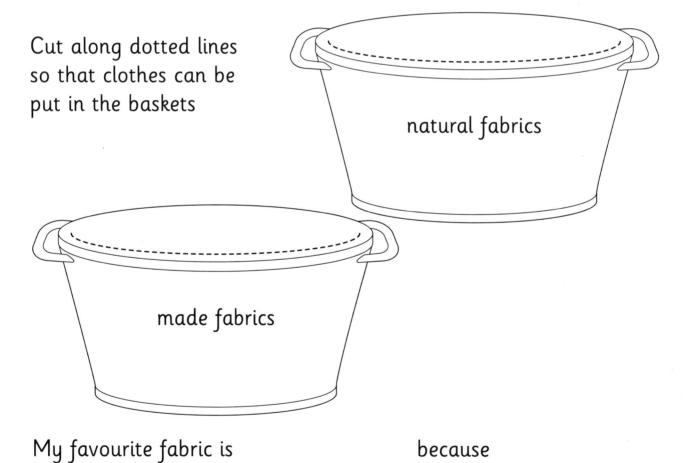

natural fabrics

made fabrics

My favourite fabric is _____ because _____

_____

_____

Name: _____ Date: _____

A Use of materials

Give two examples for which each material is used

Raw material	Used for
wood	1 _____ 2 _____
glass	1 _____ 2 _____
sheet steel	1 _____ 2 _____
cotton	1 _____ 2 _____
latex	1 _____ 2 _____

Name: _____ Date: _____

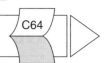

| B | Use of materials | C64 |

Give two examples for which each material is used?

Raw material	Used for
rubber sheeting	1 _____ 2 _____
wood	1 _____ 2 _____
iron ore	1 _____ 2 _____
clay	1 _____ 2 _____
wool	1 _____ 2 _____

Name: _____ Date: _____

A | Reversible/irreversible changes

How long does it take for ice-cubes to melt completely?

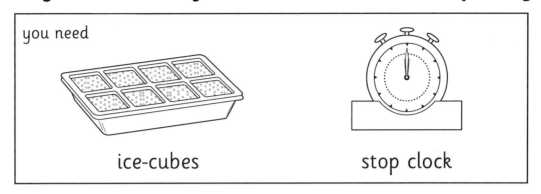

you need

ice-cubes   stop clock

Location	Time taken	
	minutes	seconds
a On table		
b In shade near window		
c In the sun		
d On radiator		
e In cupboard		
f In fridge		

Can you stop an ice-cube from melting?   yes ☐   no ☐

If yes, how? _____

_____

_____

Can you remake an ice-cube from one that has melted?

_____

_____

Name: _____ Date: _____

B | Reversible/irreversible changes

Describe flour _____

_____

_____

Describe salt _____

_____

Describe water _____

_____

warm water

120 g flour   60 g salt

What happens when they are mixed and baked? _____

_____

_____

Can you get the flour, salt and water back as separate ingredients?

yes ☐   no ☐

If yes – How?   If no – Why? _____

_____

_____

Name: _____ Date: _____

A | Solids, liquids and gases

Draw the particles in a solid, a liquid and a gas

solid   **liquid**   **gas**

How do you know the materials (below) are solids, liquids or gases?

Say what they are, describe the properties of each

name	solid, liquid or gas?	the properties are
steel		_____ _____
water		_____ _____
air		_____ _____
rubber		_____ _____
bubbles in fizzy drink		_____ _____

B | Solids, liquids and gases

C68

Weigh these unopened cans of drink carefully
Record the results

| fizzy drink 1 | fizzy drink 2 | fizzy drink 3 | still drink 1 | still drink 2 | still drink3 |

Now open them all Leave for 24 hours

What do you think will happen? _____

_____

_____

Weigh and record again

| fizzy drink 1 | fizzy drink 2 | fizzy drink 3 | still drink 1 | still drink 2 | still drink 3 |

What happened? _____

_____

_____

Name: _____ Date: _____

| A | Filtration – separating mixtures | 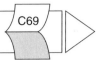 |

Use the equipment shown below
Design a filtering system to purify the muddy water
Label the diagram carefully

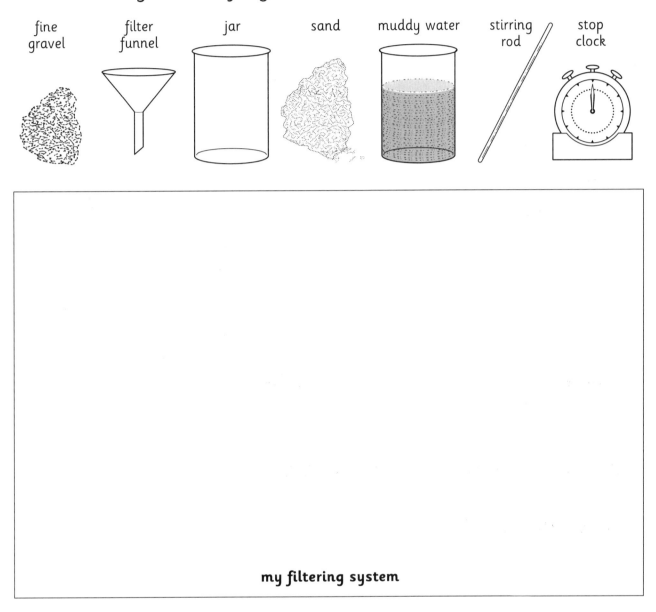

fine gravel   filter funnel   jar   sand   muddy water   stirring rod   stop clock

my filtering system

Can you suggest how your design could be improved to make the water even cleaner?

_____

_____

_____

_____

Name: _____ Date: _____

| B | Filtration – separating mixtures |

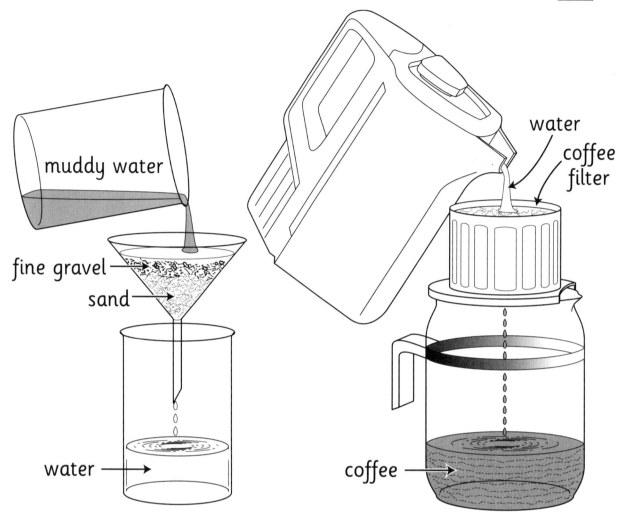

muddy water

fine gravel

sand

water

water
coffee
filter

coffee

The two pictures show two methods of filtration

How are they similar? _____

_____

_____

_____

_____

How are they different? _____

_____

_____

_____

_____

Name: _____ Date: _____

AT3 Level 4

A **Evaporation and condensation**

C71

What happens to the water in
the kettle when it is heated?

_____
_____
_____
_____

_____

Draw a diagram
to show the inside
of the kettle ➡

What will be seen on the cold plate as the kettle boils? Why?

_____
_____
_____

Complete the sentence

When the kettle_____ , water is _____ as steam, when

the steam cools on the plate it _____ back into _____ .

Give two more examples of evaporation and condensation

_____
_____
_____

Name: _____ Date: _____

B | **Evaporation and condensation** 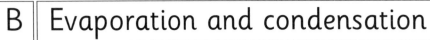 C72

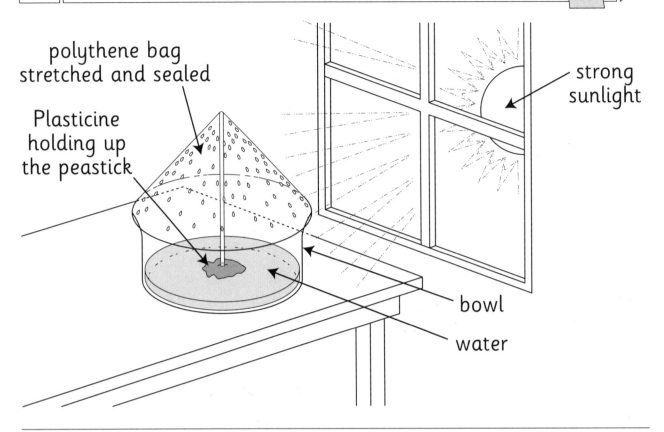

polythene bag
stretched and sealed

Plasticine
holding up
the peastick

strong
sunlight

bowl

water

Look at this diagram and label it using these words:
sea, lake, evaporation, condensation, snow, rain

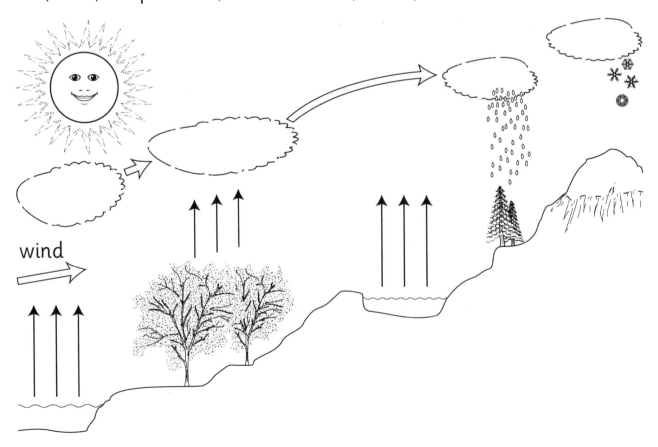

wind

Name: _____ Date: _____

| A | Are changes reversible or irreversible? | C73 |

Change	Is the change reversible or irreversible? Explain why
1 burning matches	reversible ✓ [ ] irreversible ✓ [ ]
2 melting candle wax	reversible ✓ [ ] irreversible ✓ [ ]
3 a burning electric fire	reversible ✓ [ ] irreversible ✓ [ ]
4 casting with plaster of Paris	reversible ✓ [ ] irreversible ✓ [ ]
5 producing steam from a kettle	reversible ✓ [ ] irreversible ✓ [ ]
6 making a bar of chocolate	reversible ✓ [ ] irreversible ✓ [ ]

Name: _____ Date: _____

| **B** | **Are changes reversible or irreversible?** |

Change	**Is the change reversible or irreversible? Explain why**
1 burning a camp stove	reversible ✓ ☐ irreversible ✓ ☐ _____ _____
2 making a nail rusty	reversible ✓ ☐ irreversible ✓ ☐ _____ _____
3 burning a wood fire	reversible ✓ ☐ irreversible ✓ ☐ _____ _____
4 making clay pots	reversible ✓ ☐ irreversible ✓ ☐ _____ _____
5 making ice-cubes	reversible ✓ ☐ irreversible ✓ ☐ _____ _____
6 making fairy cakes	reversible ✓ ☐ irreversible ✓ ☐ _____ _____
7 making jelly	reversible ✓ ☐ irreversible ✓ ☐ _____ _____

C74

Name: _____ Date: _____

A │ Metallic properties

C75

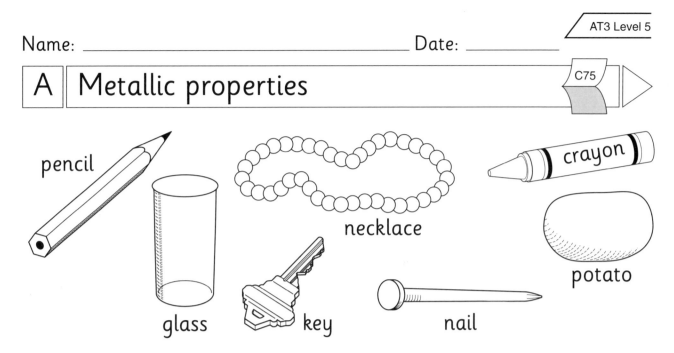

pencil

necklace

crayon

glass   key   nail   potato

Which of these do you think will conduct electricity?

_____

_____

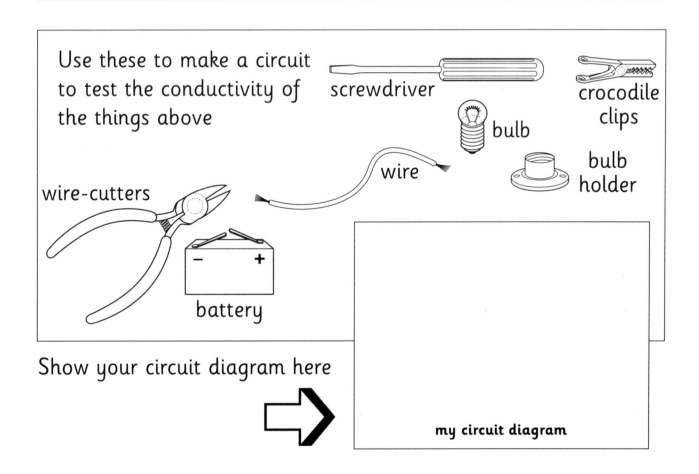

Use these to make a circuit to test the conductivity of the things above

screwdriver

crocodile clips

bulb

wire

bulb holder

wire-cutters

battery

– +

Show your circuit diagram here

my circuit diagram

Test your predictions using your circuit. What did you find out?

_____

_____

_____

B Metallic properties

C76

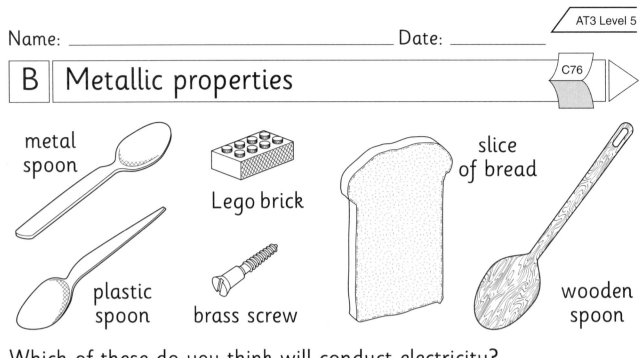

metal spoon

Lego brick

slice of bread

plastic spoon

brass screw

wooden spoon

Which of these do you think will conduct electricity?

_____

_____

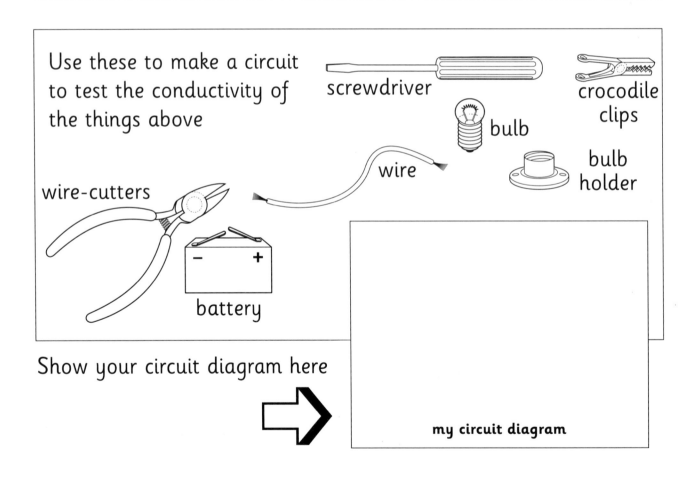

Use these to make a circuit to test the conductivity of the things above

screwdriver

crocodile clips

bulb

bulb holder

wire

wire-cutters

battery

Show your circuit diagram here

my circuit diagram

Test your predictions using your circuit. What did you find out?

_____

_____

Name: _____ Date: _____

A | Some metals are magnetic

copper wire

magnet

key

paperclip   ring

can

hairclip

coins   washer

Which of these metal objects do you predict will be attracted to the magnet?

	paperclip	copper wire	key	5p coin	2p coin	hairclip	can	washer	ring
will be attracted									
will not be attracted									

Test your predictions

	paperclip	copper wire	key	5p coin	2p coin	hairclip	can	washer	ring
is attracted									
is not attracted									

What is your conclusion? _____

_____

_____

B | Some metals are magnetic

C78

magnet

aluminium foil

bulldog clip

iron filings

safety pin

plastic comb

metal ruler

scissors

Which of these objects do you predict will be attracted to the magnet?

	safety pin	aluminium foil	plastic comb	iron filings	bulldog clip	scissors	metal ruler
will be attracted							
will not be attracted							

Test your predictions

	safety pin	aluminium foil	plastic comb	iron filings	bulldog clip	scissors	metal ruler
is attracted							
is not attracted							

What is your conclusion? _____

_____

_____

_____

Name: _____ Date: _____

A ‖ Evaporation

1 **2** **3**

(a) fridge **(b)** radiator **(c)** cool cupboard

Three identical pieces of water-saturated cloth are placed
(a) in a fridge, **(b)** on a hot radiator, **(c)** in a cool cupboard

Which cloth will dry quickest? Why? _____

_____

_____

_____

_____

Which cloth will dry slowest? Why? _____

_____

_____

_____

_____

Name: _____ Date: _____

B ‖ Evaporation

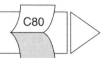

C80

Place a measuring jug with exactly 1 litre of water in it on the window sill in direct sunlight on a Monday

Check from Monday to Friday at the same time every day
Record the levels as a bar chart on the diagram above

Can you explain what happens over the five days?

_____

_____

_____

_____

Name: _____ Date: _____

A Separating mixtures

C81

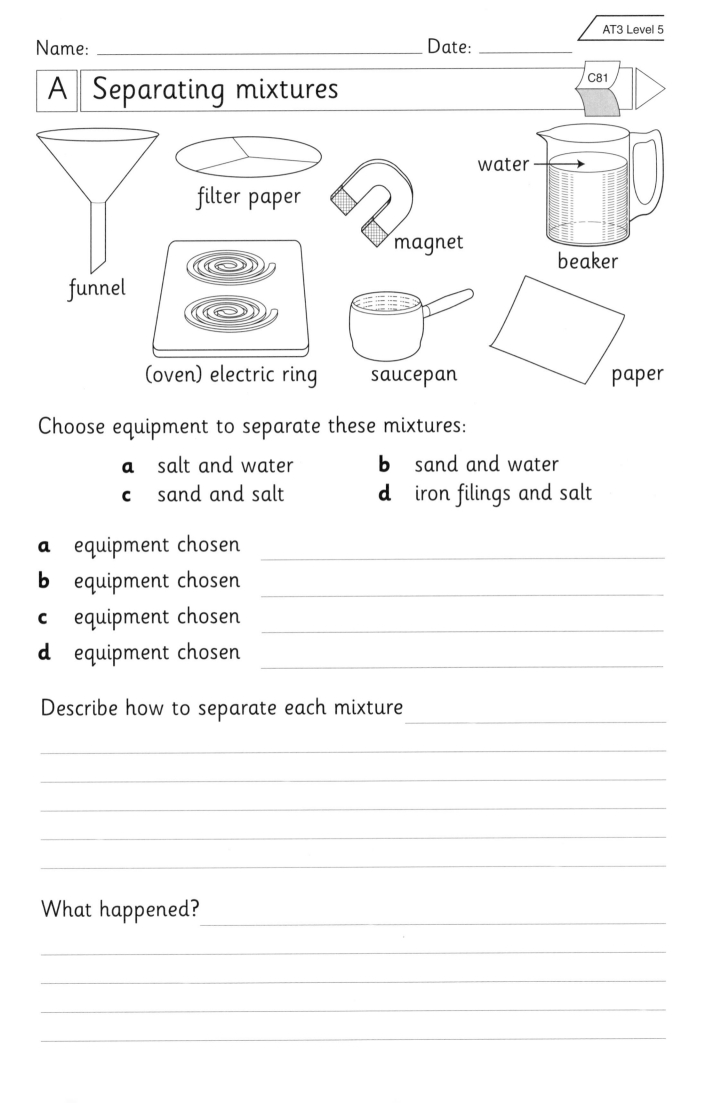

funnel

filter paper

magnet

water →

beaker

(oven) electric ring

saucepan

paper

Choose equipment to separate these mixtures:

a salt and water   **b** sand and water

c sand and salt   **d** iron filings and salt

a equipment chosen _____

b equipment chosen _____

c equipment chosen _____

d equipment chosen _____

Describe how to separate each mixture _____

_____

_____

_____

_____

_____

What happened? _____

_____

_____

_____

Name: _____ Date: _____

B | Separating mixtures

C82

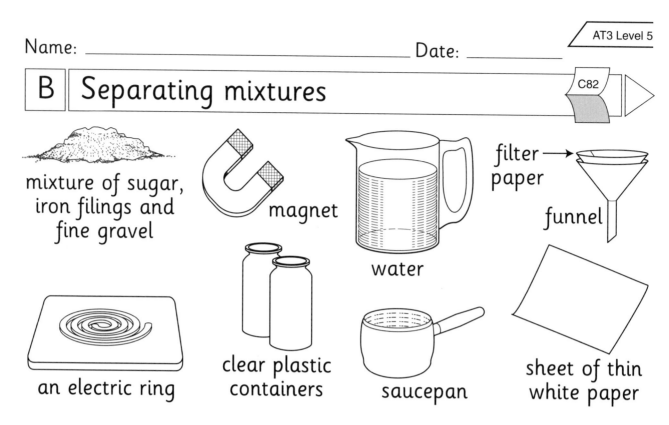

mixture of sugar, iron filings and fine gravel

magnet

water

filter paper

funnel

an electric ring

clear plastic containers

saucepan

sheet of thin white paper

Using this equipment, how would you separate a mixture of granulated white sugar, iron filings and fine gravel?
Use diagrams to explain your method

Test your ideas, record and explain what happened

_____

_____

_____

_____

_____

Name: _____ Date: _____

A | Comparing effects

C83

Use some 'sunglasses' with red lenses to look at a red pot,
a yellow flower and a blue book. What do the colours look like?
Colour carefully using pencils

Take the 'sunglasses' off
What do you notice about the coloured pictures?

_____

_____

_____

_____

_____

B | Comparing effects

C84

Use some 'sunglasses' with blue lenses to look at
a yellow T-shirt, a blue jug and a red balloon
What do the colours look like?
Colour carefully using pencils

Take the 'sunglasses' off
What do you notice about the coloured pictures?

_____

_____

_____

_____

_____

Name: _____ Date: _____

A ‖ Breaks in circuits

Will the bulb light in these circuits?

Can you say why or why not? Use diagrams to explain if you wish

Circuit	Does the bulb light? Why?
1 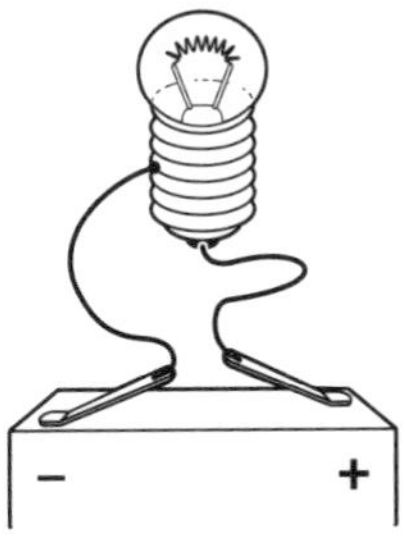	
2 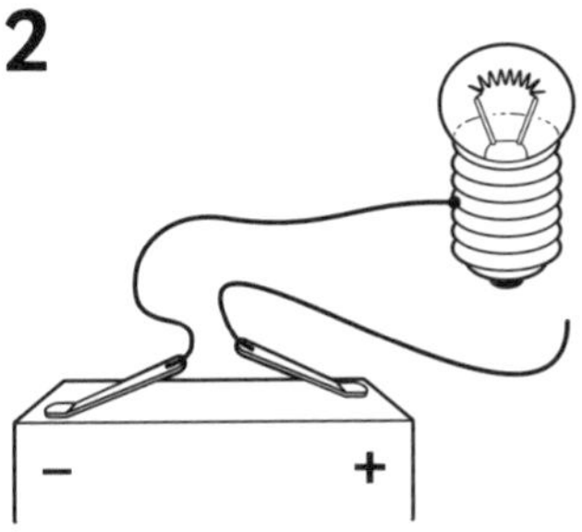	
3 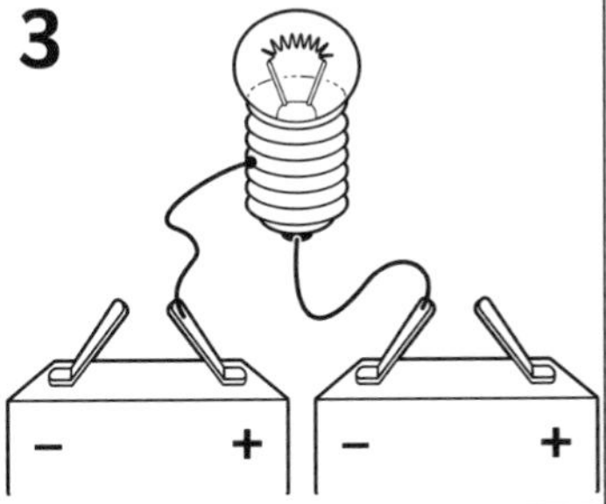	
4 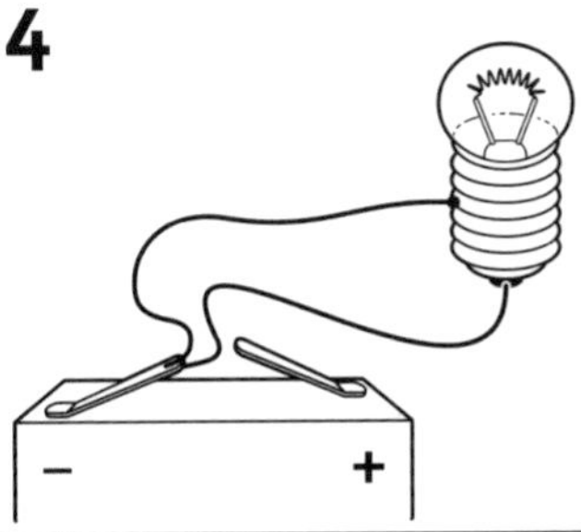	
5 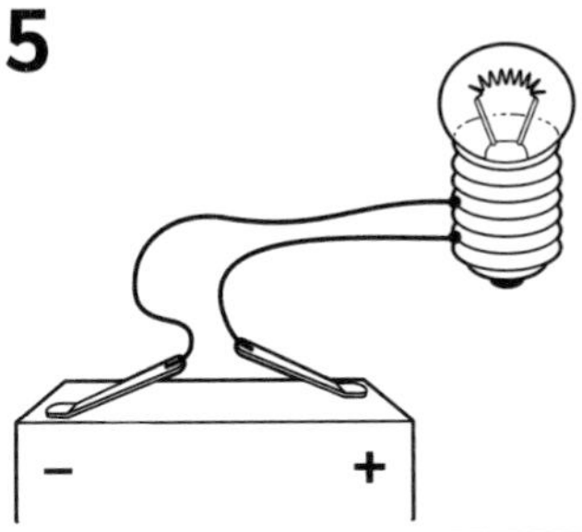	

Now test your predictions by making the circuits

B | **Breaks in circuits**

C86

Will the bulb light in these circuits?
Can you say why or why not? Use diagrams to explain if you wish

Circuit	Does the bulb light? Why?
1	
2	
3	
4	
5	

Now make the circuits and test your predictions

Name: _____ Date: _____

A Forces applied to objects

Where are the forces acting in these situations?
Show the forces using arrows and explain what is happening

Name: _____ Date: _____

B Forces applied to objects

Where are the forces acting in these situations?

Show where the forces are acting using arrows
and explain what is happening

Name: _____ Date: _____

A | Sounds over distance   C89 ▷

Which clock will be easiest to hear? Tick ✓ your choice

A   tick   ☐
         short tube

B   tick   ☐
         medium tube

C   tick   ☐
         long tube

Try it. What happened? _____

_____

_____

_____

Which of these telephones will give the loudest sound?

Tick ✓ your choice

A   =hello=   ☐

B   =hello=   ☐

C   =hello=   ☐

D =hello=   ☐

Explain your choice _____

_____

_____

Name: _____   Date: _____

| B | Sounds over distance | C90 |

Which of these will seem loudest? Tick ✓ your choice

A ☐

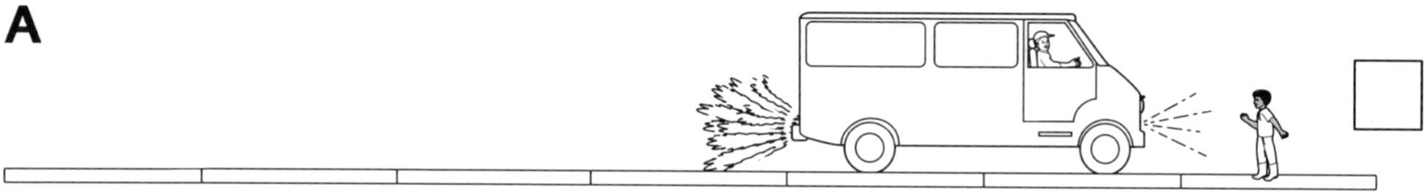

B ☐

C ☐

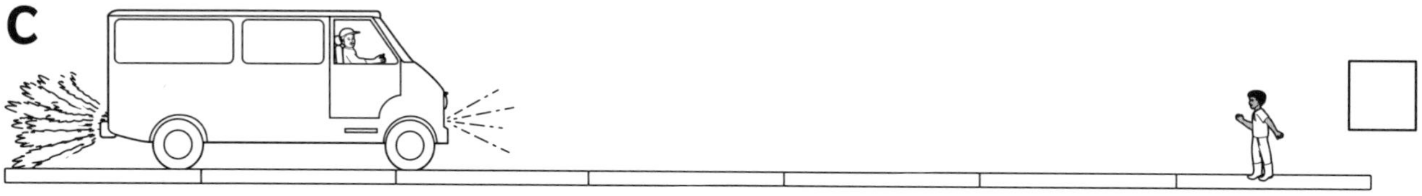

Why? _____

_____

Which of these will seem quietest? Tick ✓ your choice

A ☐

B ☐

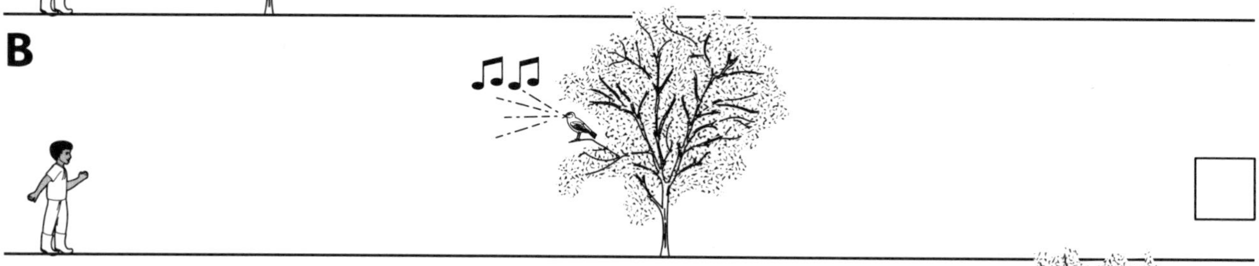

C ☐

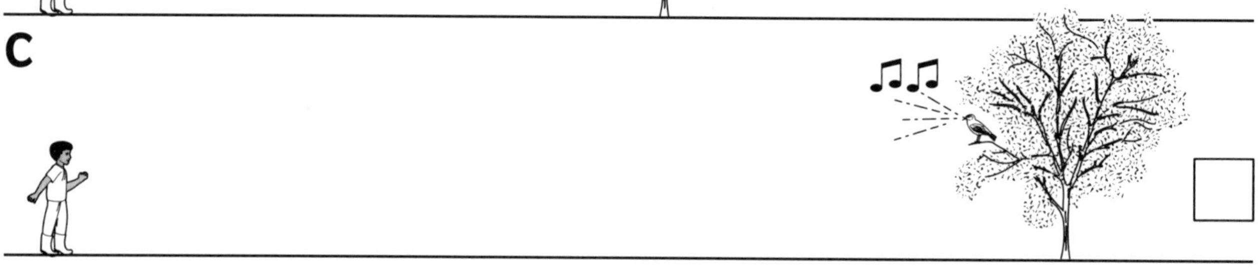

Why? _____

_____

Name: _____ Date: _____

A │ Switches in circuits

Look at these circuits and answer each of the questions

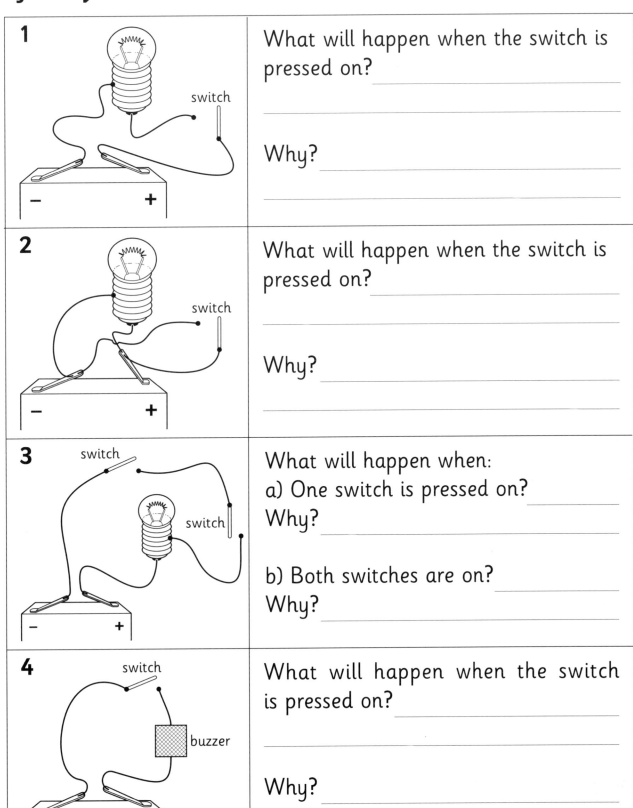

1

What will happen when the switch is pressed on? _____

_____

Why? _____

_____

2

What will happen when the switch is pressed on? _____

_____

Why? _____

_____

3

What will happen when:
a) One switch is pressed on? _____
Why? _____

b) Both switches are on? _____
Why? _____

4

What will happen when the switch is pressed on? _____

_____

Why? _____

_____

Name: ______________________ Date: __________ AT4 Level 4

B Switches in circuits

C92

Can you make a switch to control a bulb in a circuit so that it can be turned on and off? Draw the circuit diagram below

How will it work? ______________________

____

____

Design and draw the circuit diagram using a switch for either:
a) a flashing model lighthouse, **b)** a morse code machine or
c) a model with flashing eye

How will it work? ______________________

____

____

Name: _____ Date: _____

| A | The sun's position during the day | 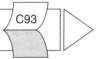 |

Draw where the sun will be at these three different times of day

9 am   **midday**   **3 pm**

Draw this boy's shadow
(think about its length and position)

Draw the sun at midday,
then draw the boy's shadow
Is it different to the shadow you
drew above?

_____

Why is it different? _____

_____

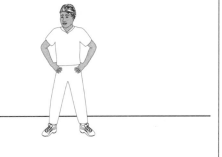

Name: _____ Date: _____

| B | The sun's position during the day | C94 |

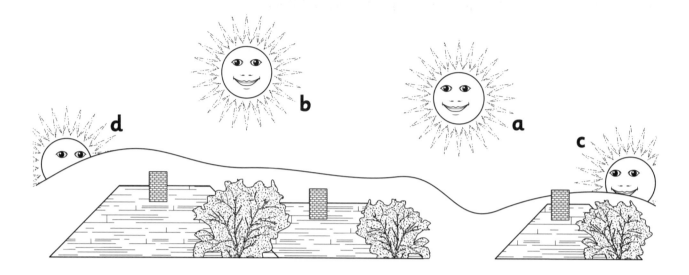

What time do you think it is when the sun is in these four different positions?
Match the letters of the sun with the time, using arrows.

a	9.15 am
b	3.15 pm
c	1.30 pm
d	11.45 am

About what time do you think it is when the stick forms these shadows?

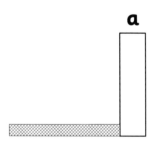

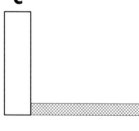

time _____   time _____   time _____

At what time of day is the shortest shadow formed? Why?

_____

_____

Name: _____ Date: _____

A | Magnetic forces

How do these magnetic games work?

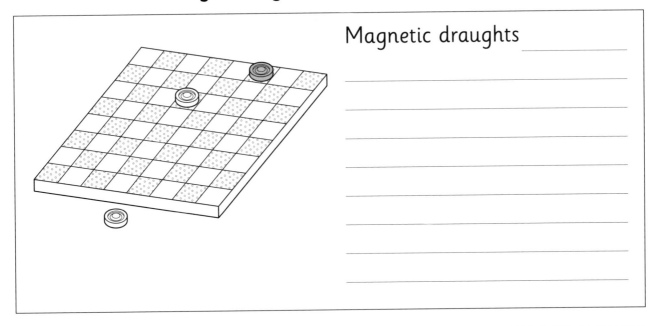

Magnetic draughts _____

_____

_____

_____

_____

_____

_____

_____

_____

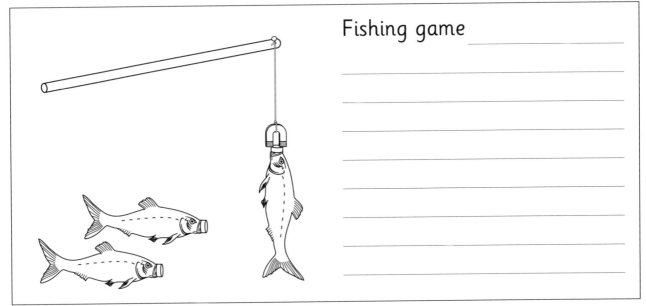

Fishing game _____

_____

_____

_____

_____

_____

_____

_____

Can you think of other games that work like these?

_____

_____

Can you invent one? _____

_____

_____

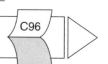

B ║ Magnetic forces

The north pole of a magnet is brought closer to a magnetized pin on a float. The pointed end of the pin is also a north pole. What will happen as the magnet is brought closer? Why?

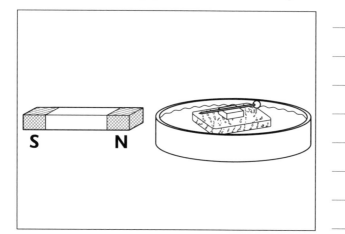

_____
_____
_____
_____
_____
_____
_____

What happens as these two cars approach each other? Why?

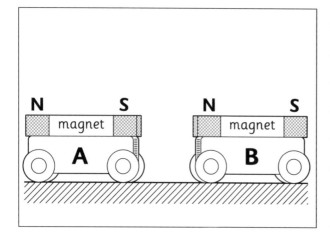

_____
_____
_____
_____
_____
_____
_____

Can you devise a test to find out if magnet **A** or **B** is the strongest? Draw a picture of it

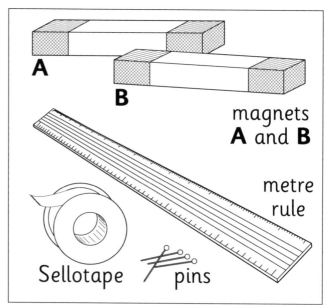

magnets **A** and **B**

metre rule

Sellotape   pins

Name: _____   Date: _____

A | Motion and gravity

C97

If a potato and a similarly sized fir-cone are dropped from the same height, which will hit the floor first? Why? _____

_____

_____

_____

_____

1.5 m

Test it. Were you right? _____

If a small potato and a large potato are dropped from the same height, which will hit the floor first? Why?

_____

_____

_____

_____

1.5 m

Test it. Were you right? _____

What would happen if you used a feather instead of a small potato?
Why? _____

_____

Test it. Were you right? _____

Name: _____ Date: _____

B | Motion and gravity

Draw arrows to explain what forces are acting on this ball after it has been thrown.

Can you explain what is happening?

_____

_____

_____

_____

_____

_____

The soldier is standing at the top of a ladder.

Why might he fall down?

_____

_____

_____

_____

_____

_____

What forces are acting on this glass? Draw arrows to show them.

Explain what is happening:

_____

_____

_____

_____

Name: _____ Date: _____

A │ Friction affects motion

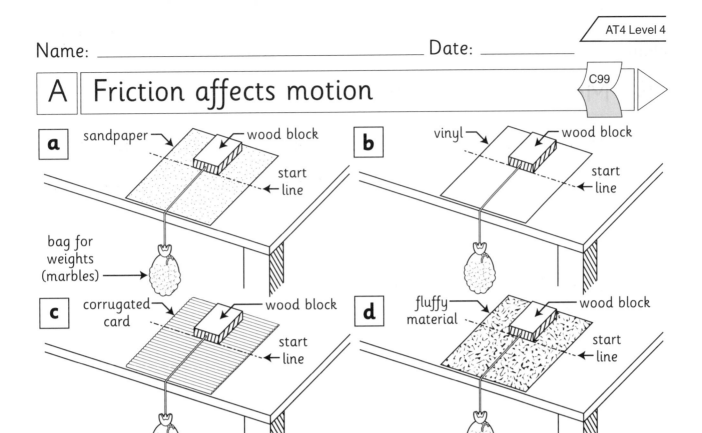

Predict which block will need the most mass and which will need the least mass to move it to the edge of the table

Tick ✓ your choices

	a	b	c	d
needs the most mass				
needs the least mass				

Now test it. What did you find?
(You can add mass to each empty bag until the wooden block moves – use marbles as mass. Count them.)

	a	b	c	d
mass needed (number of marbles)				

Were they different? Why? _____

_____

Name: _____ Date: _____

B | Friction affects motion

C100

a

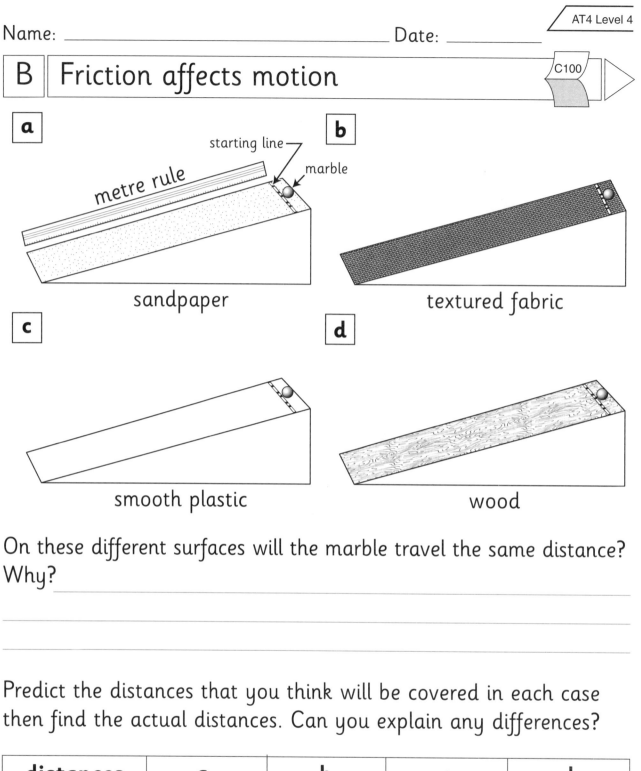

starting line

marble

metre rule

sandpaper

b

textured fabric

c

smooth plastic

d

wood

On these different surfaces will the marble travel the same distance?
Why? _____

_____

Predict the distances that you think will be covered in each case
then find the actual distances. Can you explain any differences?

distances	a	b	c	d
predicted				
actual				

_____

_____

_____

Name: _____ Date: _____

| A | Light and the formation of shadows |

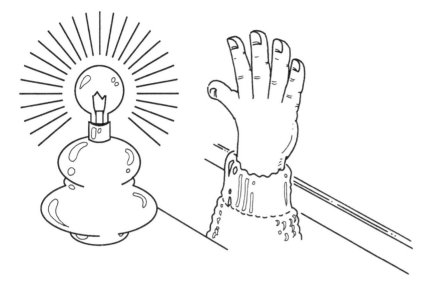

What will be seen on the wall? Complete the wall picture.
Why does this happen? _____

_____

_____

Draw the shadows of these trees

Why are these shadows formed? _____

_____

Where else will shadows be formed? _____

_____

Name: _____ Date: _____

B | **Light and the formation of shadows** C102

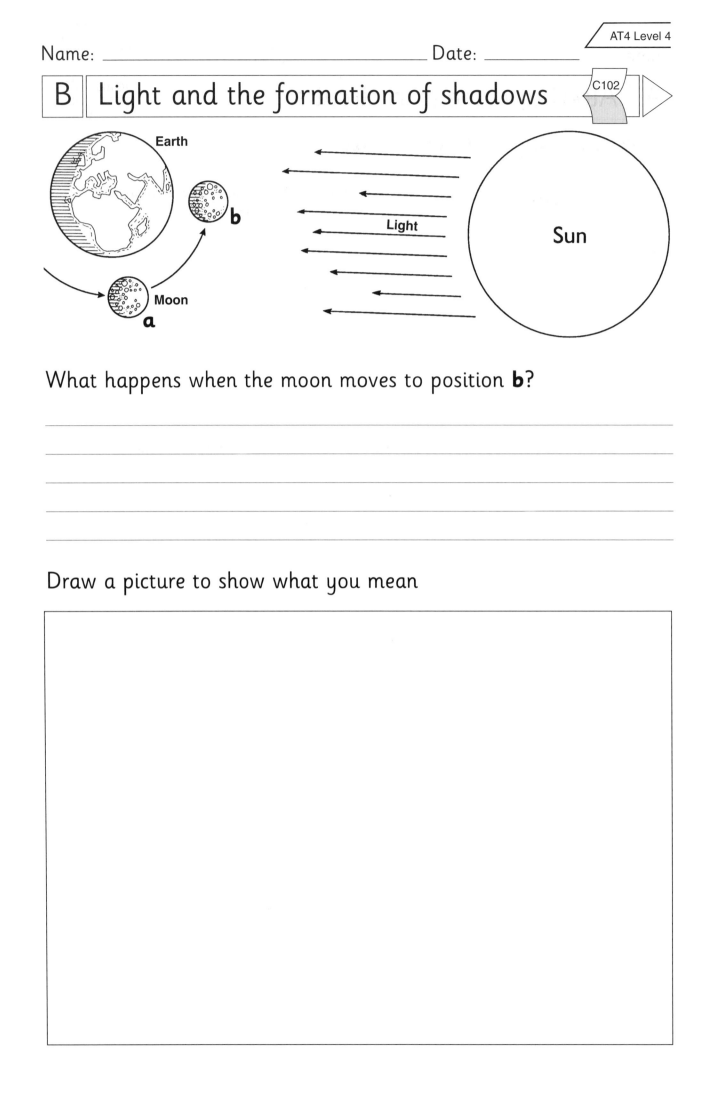

Earth

Moon

a

b

Light

Sun

What happens when the moon moves to position **b**?

_____

_____

_____

_____

_____

Draw a picture to show what you mean

Name: _____ Date: _____

| A | Altering current in circuits |

Look carefully at these circuits

circuit	What will happen in these circuits? Why?
a	_____ _____ _____ _____ _____ _____
b	**How does the brightness of the bulbs in these circuits – (b), (c) and (d) – compare to (a)?** _____ _____ _____ _____
c	_____ _____ _____ _____ _____ _____
d	_____ _____ _____ _____ _____

Name: _____ Date: _____

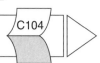

| B | Altering current in circuits |

Look carefully at these circuits

circuit	What will happen in these circuits? Why?
a	_____ _____ _____ _____ _____ _____
b	How does the brightness of the bulbs in these circuits – (b), (c), (d) and (e) – compare to (a)? _____ _____ _____
c	_____ _____ _____ _____ _____
d	_____ _____ _____ _____
e	_____ _____ _____ _____

| A | Altering pitch and loudness of sound | C105 |

Plucking a stretched elastic band produces a sound.
If the same elastic band is stretched over three different box lids,
what kind of sound will result when the band is plucked?

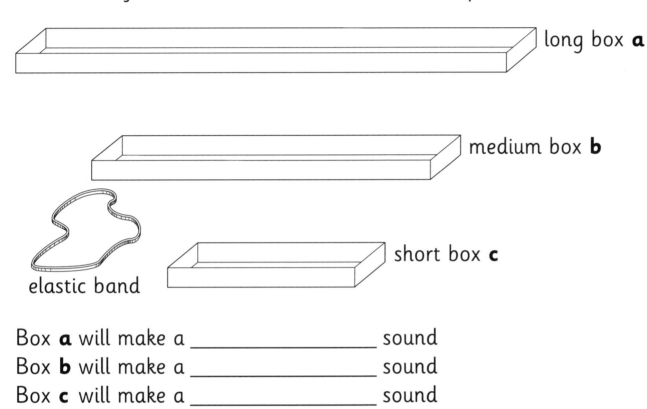

long box **a**

medium box **b**

short box **c**

elastic band

Box **a** will make a _____ sound
Box **b** will make a _____ sound
Box **c** will make a _____ sound

Fill the jars with water so that the pitch will be high, medium and
low when tapped. Draw the level on the picture.

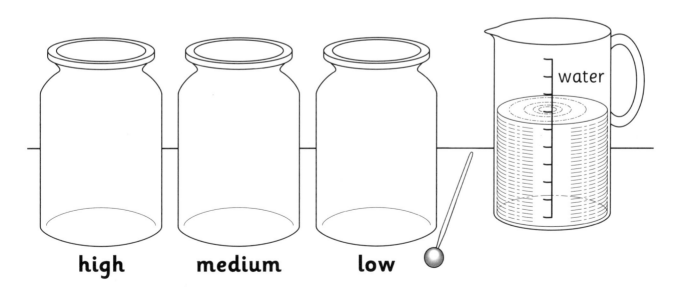

high   **medium**   **low**   water

Fill the jars until you can play the first line of three blind mice

Name: _____ Date: _____

B ‖ Altering pitch and loudness of sound

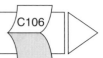

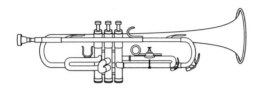

How does a trumpet make a sound of different pitch? _____

_____

_____

_____

How are the sounds made higher or lower on a guitar? _____

_____

_____

_____

How are sounds made louder or quieter on a guitar? _____

_____

_____

_____

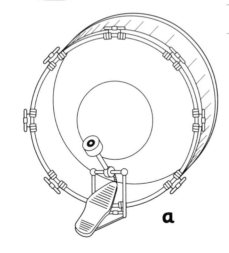

a

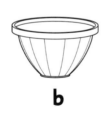

b

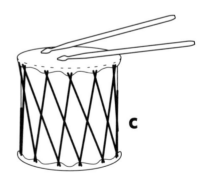

c

Describe the sounds produced by these drums

a _____

b _____

c _____

Why do the sounds change according to how they are struck? _____

_____

_____

_____

Name: _____ Date: _____

A | Forces balanced on stationary objects

a What are the forces acting on these stationary pushchairs?
Show them with arrows

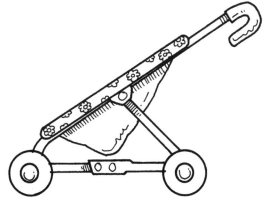

b Explain any differences by making notes and drawings

_____

_____

_____

_____

_____

_____

_____

_____

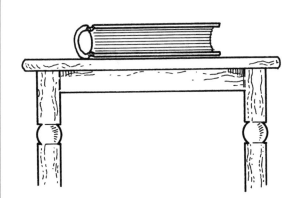

Explain the forces acting that
keep the book stationary

_____

_____

_____

_____

_____

Where are the forces acting
on this book?
Show the forces with arrows

_____

_____

B Forces balanced on stationary objects C108

a What forces are acting on these stationary toy trucks?
Show with arrows

b Explain any differences between the two trucks by making
notes and drawings

_____

_____

_____

_____

_____

_____

_____

_____

_____

Where are forces acting on
the computer, monitor,
keyboard and table?
Show the forces with arrows

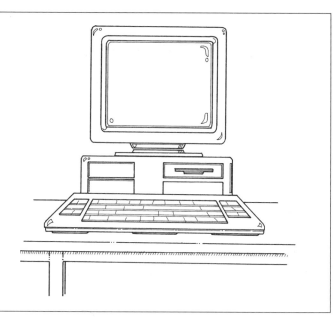

Name: _____ Date: _____

| A | Seeing objects |

Use arrows to explain the direction light is travelling in

Explain how this woman can read her newspaper _____

_____

_____

_____

Draw a picture of light entering an eye

Name: _____ Date: _____

| B | Seeing objects |

C110

Cat's-eyes help drivers to drive safely at night
How do Cat's-eyes work?
Draw a diagram to show the direction of light
(Include the driver's eyes, the headlamp and Cat's-eyes)

_____

_____

_____

_____

Name: _____ Date: _____

| A | Effects caused by the earth moving |

This diagram (not to scale) shows the position of the earth in relation to the sun in our summer and winter

N

21 June

sun

N

21 December

S

Explain why it is hotter in the summer than in the winter
Use diagrams

_____

_____

_____

Does the north pole get six months daylight in our summer
or winter?   Tick ✓ summer ☐   winter ☐
Why? _____

_____

Explain why, during the summer, Britain gets a long day and a short night _____

_____

_____

_____

Name: _____ Date: _____

B | Effects caused by the earth moving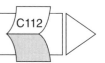

The diagram shows the position of the earth, sun and moon as the moon moves round the earth during a lunar month

sun	sun	sun	sun	sun	sun	sun	sun
				earth ↓ 🌍 moon ↑			
				E full moon			H old moon
A	**B**	**C**	**D**	**E** full moon	**F**	**G**	**H** old moon

Boxes **E** and **H** have drawings to show how the moon looks from earth. Make accurate drawings for all the other boxes.

The earth's axis is tilted to the plane of its orbit around the sun
Draw a diagram to show the position of the earth and sun if the earth's axis were not tilted

What would be the main effects?

_____
_____
_____
_____
_____
_____
_____
_____

Record Sheet 1 Class Record

Class	Level		Date		
			Teacher's name		

Name	AT1	AT2	AT3	AT4

Record Sheet 2 Child's Record

Name		Date of birth	Teacher's Initials	

AT1

Level 2	Date	Level 4	Date	Level 5	Date
1 Respond/predict		6 Fair test/variable 1		9 Predict	
2 Describe/record		7 Fair test/variable 2		10 Key factors	
Level 3	**Date**	8 Patterns/trends		11 Line graph	
3 Answer/prediction					
4 Fair test					
5 Patterns/report					

AT2

Level 2	Date	Level 3	Date	Level 5	Date
1 Plant growth		6 Living/non-living		12 Diet	
2 Animal life process		7 Suitable homes		13 Organ function/human	
3 Living things/homes		**Level 4**	**Date**	14 Organ function/plant	
4 Animal/plant		8 Human organs		15 Life cycle/human	
5 Reproduction		9 Plant organs		16 Life cycle/plants	
		10 Group living things		17 Preferred habitats	
		11 Food chains		18 Classification	

AT3

Level 2	Date	Level 4	Date	Level 5	Date
1 Common materials		5 Solids, liquids, gases		9 Metallic properties	
2 Material properties		6 Filtration		10 Magnetic metals	
Level 3	**Date**	7 Evaporate/condense		11 Evaporation	
3 Use of materials		8 Reversible/irreversible		12 Separate mixtures	
4 Reversible/irreversible					

AT4

Level 2	Date	Level 4	Date	Level 5	Date
1 Compare effects		5 Switches in circuits		11 Altering current	
Level 3	**Date**	6 Sun's position		12 Altering pitch/loudness	
2 Breaks in circuits		7 Magnetic forces		13 Balanced forces	
3 Forces		8 Motion/gravity		14 Seeing objects	
4 Sound/distance		9 Friction		15 Earth's movement	
		10 Shadows			

Record Sheet 2 Child's Record